英文該怎麼學才對？

　　有位同學跟我說，他的老師認為「文法寶典」太詳細了。事實上，同學只要看第一篇「文法概論」，就知道整個文法的輪廓。看到同學的教科書，非常難過，同學看不懂，老師也往往看不懂，把簡單的解說變複雜，甚至用英文來解說，更造成學習的障礙。有些書取材自美國的文法書，翻譯得硬梆梆，我覺得，那些美國作者自己也不很懂文法，所寫的文法規則只是概要，常忽略例外的情形。設身處地想想看，太為難美國作者了，有幾個中國人能編出一套中文文法？

　　編者從事英語教學已有 40 年，每一堂課都戰戰兢兢，深怕被同學淘汰，碰到文法難題，一般書上查不到的，都徹底研究，因為這就是上課最精彩的部分。例如：老師說「讓步子句」，學生怎麼聽得懂？要補充說明，對主要子句所說的話，語氣上加以退讓的，叫作「讓步子句」，像 however、although 等引導的副詞子句。好的老師上課幽默，深入淺出，學生一聽就懂，好的書籍版面美觀，要讓同學一看就懂，裡面要有靈魂，要有生命。「文法寶典」就是編者從教學上遭遇的難題而產生的，同學在考試中所碰到的大部分難題，都可在「文法寶典」中找到答案。

　　文法學得不完全，反倒是學英文的一個障礙。「劉毅英文」最近提出一個激勵員工的口號，**Time is money, efficiency is life**. 這句話外國人和網站上都認可，而 money 後面沒有連接詞，會被懂點文法的人誤解成錯誤，我們不得不勉強改成：Time is money. Efficiency is life. 其實，這種口號、諺語等常用省略句的形式，像：

> Trust me, you can make it. (相信我，你做得到。)
> Waste not, want not. (不浪費，不會窮。)
> Nothing venture, nothing have. (不入虎穴，焉得虎子。)
> Out of sight, out of mind. (眼不見，心不念；離久情疏。)
> United we stand, divided we fall. (團結則立，分散則倒。)

碰到這類沒有連接詞的句子，應該把它當作例外來看。

　　有人只學了二個句子之間一定要有連接詞，忽略了它的例外部分，寫句子、說話，都因為所學的文法規則而受限制。大部分的美國人，也因此不太敢寫文章，甚至對自己所寫的英文沒有信心。

英文句子的範圍無限大，再多的文法家，也無法將美國人所説的話、所寫的文章，歸納成規則，所以，我們在日常生活中，聽到與自己所學文法相矛盾的時候，不要認爲外國人錯，一定要找出原因來。例如：美國人吃完飯，準備結帳，通常會説 We're done.（我們吃完了。）如果你學的文法不完全，你就會懷疑，這句話爲什麼用被動式呢？不敢模仿。碰到這種情況，除了查閱「文法寶典」之外，還可以查閱「一口氣英語」。

苦練的英文最美

學英文最簡單的方法，就是背「一口氣英語」和「一口氣英語演講」，「一口氣英語」每句話都是美國人口語的精華，三句爲一組，九句爲一段，九句話只要背到五秒鐘之內，就終身不會忘，唯有不會忘，才能累積，否則，背了後面，忘記前面。對於不會説英語的人，既然要學英語，就趁這個機會，學習最悦耳的語言。例如，一般人只會説 Thank you.，背了「一口氣英語」，你會一口氣説出好幾句：Thank you so much. You're so thoughtful. I'm really grateful. 等。用「一口氣英語」書中的句子，你説出來的話熱情又體貼，周圍的人都會喜歡你，美國人也會認爲你是有教養的人，因爲苦練的英文最美。

和外國人淺談，用「一口氣英語」，和外國人深談，用「一口氣英語演講」。背了一千多個英文句子，和 20 篇英語演講，就可以排列組合成無限多的演講，會演講自然會説話，**用自己背過的句子，説起來有信心**。用自己所知道的有限文法規則來造句，非常危險，**合乎文法，不見得合乎美國人的習慣用法**，甚至錯誤，例如：Diamond cut diamond.（硬碰硬；勢均力敵。）一般人以爲諺語要用現在式動詞，這裡爲什麼不寫成 cuts 呢？詳見「文法寶典」p.327，「英文諺語辭典」p.84。

看英文小説，也是學英文的好方法，要選擇自己看得下去的英文小説，小説的前 20 頁要徹底看懂，每一個字、每一個句子、人名、地名都要很熟悉，再繼續看下去，就可以不要再查字典了。例如，John Grisham 曾當過律師，他寫的小説比較嚴謹，不會有錯誤，又好看，他的有名作品有：*The Firm*，*The Client*，*The Pelican Brief*，*A Time to Kill* 等。出國旅行或無聊的時候，看英文小説能夠提高你對英文的興趣，增加閱讀能力，可以先從 *The Firm* 看起，書裡的劇情，會引導你繼續看下去。一個人無聊的時候，背一背「一口氣英語」、「一口氣英語演講」，旅行回來，你的英文一定會進步神速。

劉 毅

CONTENTS

第九篇　連接詞（Conjunctions）

第一章　概論

第二章　對等連接詞

練習一～十四

【附錄 —— 英文法盲點講座】

第八篇　動狀詞（Verbals）

第一章　不定詞（Infinitives）

Ⅰ. **定義：** 不定詞是具有名詞、形容詞及副詞性質的動詞形態，用來表示動作。與人稱及數無關。分爲<u>有 to 的不定詞</u>與<u>無 to 的不定詞</u>兩種。

Ⅱ. **形式：**

時式　＼　語態	主　動　語　態	被　動　語　態
簡　單　式	to + 原形動詞 （to write）	to be + 過去分詞 （to be written）
進　行　式	to be + 現在分詞 （to be writing）	無
完　成　式	to have + 過去分詞 （to have written）	to have been + 過去分詞 （to have been written）
完成進行式	to have been + 現在分詞 （to have been writing）	無

否定形態： not (to) + 原形動詞；never (to) + 原形動詞

Ⅲ. **不定詞片語：**

不定詞 + {　受詞字群　補語字群　副詞字群　} = 不定詞片語

下列均爲不定詞片語：

<u>to pretend</u> <u>not to see me</u>（假裝沒有看見我）
　不　定　詞　　受　　　詞

<u>to become</u> <u>a teacher</u>（當老師）
　不　定　詞　補　　語

<u>to study</u> <u>hard</u>（用功讀書）
　不　定　詞　副詞

Ⅳ. **不定詞意義上的主詞：**

1. **不表明其爲不定詞意義上的主詞的情況：**

    ⑴ 主要動詞的主詞即不定詞意義上的主詞時。

    I want *to go* hunting with you.（我想和你一起去打獵。）

    → I 是主要動詞 want 的主詞，也是不定詞 to go 意義上的主詞。

    I asked *to speak* to the manager.（我要求與經理談話。）

    → I 是主要動詞 asked 的主詞，也是不定詞 to speak 意義上的主詞。

(2) 主要動詞的受詞即不定詞意義上的主詞時。

I will get *someone to carry* your baggage. (我將叫人搬運你的行李。)
→ 主要動詞的受詞 someone，做不定詞 to carry 意義上的主詞。
The doctor advised *me* not *to drink* too much. (醫生勸我不要喝太多酒。)
→ 主要動詞的受詞 me，做不定詞 to drink 意義上的主詞。

(3) 由句子前後關係可知不定詞之意義上的主詞時。

I found that *to talk* with him was a waste of time. (我發現和他說話是浪費時間。)
→ 由句子前後關係可知 I 是不定詞 to talk 意義上的主詞。
He found that *to leave* the house unobserved was easy.
(他發覺讓房子空著，沒有人看守是很容易的。)
→ 由句子前後關係可知 He 是不定詞 to leave 意義上的主詞。

(4) 在一些**諺語**、**格言**或一般衆所周知的事。

To err is human, to forgive divine. (犯錯是人，寬恕是神。)
It is better to give than to receive. (施比受更有福。)
It is wrong to tell a lie. (說謊話是錯誤的。)

2. 表明其爲不定詞意義上的主詞時，用下列表示方式：

(1) for + 受詞（意義上的主詞）+ 不定詞

It is difficult *for you to read* this book. (你要讀這本書是困難的。)
= For you to read this book is difficult.
It's bad *for him to live* alone. (他獨自生活是不好的。)
It is impossible *for her to give up* drinking. (要她戒酒是不可能的。)
When will it be convenient *for me to call*? (我何時打電話方便呢？)

(2) It is + 形容詞 + of + 受詞（意義上的主詞）+ 不定詞（對 of 後的受詞稱讚或責備時，用此句型）

It is silly *of you to say* so. = You are silly to say so. (你這樣說實在太傻了。)
It is unwise *of you to live* alone. (你要獨自生活是很不明智的。)
It was bold *of her to row up* the river. (她很大膽，敢向上游划船。)
It is very kind *of you to do* so. (你這樣做實在是太好了。)

【註】下列形容詞多用於 It is⋯of⋯to 的句型

> absurd（荒謬的）, naughty（頑皮的）, bold（大膽的）, nice, brave（勇敢的）,
> polite, careful, silly, careless, stupid, clever, wicked（邪惡的）, courageous,
> wise, kind, cruel（殘忍的）, wrong, foolish（愚蠢的）, ungrateful（忘恩負義的）,
> good, unkind, grateful, impolite, honest, unwise, ill-natured（心地邪惡的）

3. 不定詞意義上的主詞之省略：

不定詞意義上的主詞泛指一般人，或一般事物時，意義上的主詞可省略或表明。
It is important to work hard. (努力是重要的。)
→ 不定詞 to work hard 意義上的主詞應是 anyone，所以若要將意義上的主詞表明即爲：
It is important for anyone to work hard.
It is time to go to school. (是該上學的時間了。)
→ 不定詞 to go 意義上的主詞是我（或我們、你等），所以若要將意義上的主詞表明即爲：
It is time for me to go to school.

V. 不定詞意義上的受詞：

1. 主要動詞的主詞即不定詞意義上的受詞。

   The river is dangerous ***to bathe in***. (在這條河裡洗澡很危險。)
   = It is dangerous to bathe in the river.

   This house must be comfortable ***to live in***. (住在這棟房子裡一定很舒適。)
   = It must be comfortable to live in this house.

   Your question is difficult ***to answer***. (你的問題很難回答。)
   = It is difficult to answer your question.

2. 被不定詞修飾的名詞或代名詞即該不定詞意義上的受詞。

   This is a hard question to answer. (這是一個很難回答的問題。)
   = This question is hard to answer.
   = It is hard to answer this question.

   She has no one to depend on. (她沒有可以依靠的人。)
   = She has no one whom she can depend on.

   【註1】 不定詞之前已有意義上的受詞，其後就不得有文法上的受詞。

   That question is difficult $\begin{cases} \text{to answer } \textit{it}. 【誤】 \\ \text{to answer.} 【正】 \end{cases}$ (那個問題很難回答。)

   【註2】 不定詞之前沒有意義上的受詞，則其後應有文法上的受詞。

   It is hard to please ***her son***. (想要討好她的兒子不容易。)
   → 不定詞 to please 之前沒有意義上的受詞，所以它的後面必須有文法上的受詞 her son.

VI. 不定詞的用法：

1. 作名詞用：即做主詞、受詞和補語。

   主詞　　副詞片語
   To cheat in examinations is punishable. (考試作弊應受處罰。)【做主詞】
   完　全　主　詞

   To err is human, ***to forgive*** divine. (犯錯是人，寬恕是神。)【做主詞】

   They planned ***to adopt*** an orphan. (他們計劃領養一個孤兒。)【做動詞的受詞】

   You forgot ***to call*** him up. (你忘了打電話給他。)【做動詞的受詞】

   He had no desire but ***to go*** abroad. (他只希望能夠出國。)【做介詞的受詞】

   He is about ***to start*** for America. (他即將動身前往美國。)【做介詞的受詞】

   The worst is still ***to come***. (最糟糕的還在後頭。)【做主詞補語】

   To see is ***to believe***. (百聞不如一見。)【做主詞補語】

   Jack ordered his brother ***not to enter*** his study. 【做受詞補語】
   (傑克命令他的弟弟不准進入他的書房。)

   They think him ***to be*** honest. (他們認為他是誠實的。)【做受詞補語】

   【註】 不定詞只能做 but, except, than, about 這四個介詞的受詞。

   He desires nothing but ***to go*** home. (他只想回家。)
   　　　　　　　　　　介詞

   They have nothing to do except ***wander about*** in the streets.
   　　　　　　　　　　　　　　　介詞

   (他們無事可做，只是在街上到處走。)(參閱 p.419 ④)

She thought of no other way out than ***to cheat***. (除了欺騙外，她想不出別的方法。)

介詞

They are about ***to start***. (他們即將動身。)

介詞

【説明】① about 只有在前面是 "be" 動詞時，才用不定詞爲其受詞，否則應使用動名詞。（比較）They talked about having a party. (他們討論舉行宴會的事情。)

② 凡在 except, but, than 之前的動詞爲 do，或慣用語時，其後可接原形不定詞爲受詞。(參照 p.419 ④)

2. **作形容詞用**：不定詞 (片語) 可當形容詞用。

(1) **限定用法：置於所修飾名詞的後面**

He is not a man ***to tell*** a lie. (他不是個說謊的人。)

He is the very man ***to do*** this work. (他就是要做這個工作的人。)

He has many things ***to tell*** you. (他有許多事情要告訴你。)

There is nothing ***to do***. (沒有事情要做。)

【註】被修飾的名詞是不定詞介詞意義上的受詞時，其介詞不可省。

He has no house ***to live in***. (他沒有房子住。)

= He has no house *which he can live in*.

上句的 house 是做不定詞裡介詞 in 意義上的受詞。必須注意的是：**此介詞 in 不能省略**，因爲不可說 *He lives the house.* (誤) 而應該說 He lives in the house. 再看下面的例句，其情形也和上句相似：

Give me a chair { *to sit.* 【誤】
{ *to sit on (or in).* 【正】 (給我一把椅子坐。)

The child has no toys { *to play.* 【誤】
{ *to play with.* 【正】 (這孩子沒有玩具可玩。)

I have enough money ***to buy the book with***. (我有足夠的錢買這本書。)

= I have enough money *with which to buy the book*. 【介詞＋關代＋不定詞＝形容詞片語】

I lit a candle ***to read by***. (我點了蠟燭藉以閱讀。)

= I lit a candle *by which to read*.

(2) **敘述用法**：是將不定詞置於不完全不及物動詞之後作爲主詞補語，此類不及物動詞有：be, seem, appear, prove, turn out, happen, look, long, remain 等。

① **be 動詞 + 不定詞**

爲一種習慣用法，用來表示預定、義務、命運、可能性、命令等意思。

He and I ***are to meet*** at the station at two o'clock.【表預定】

(他和我預定兩點鐘在車站見面。)

You ***are to pay*** your debt. (你應該付你的欠債。)【表義務】

He ***was*** *never* ***to see*** his wife or children again.【表命運】

(= It was his destiny never to see his wife or children again.)

(他命中註定再也見不到他的妻子或兒女了。)

Nothing *is to be* seen.（什麼也看不見。）【表可能性】

You *are to come* when I call.（我叫你的時候，你必須來。）【表命令】

【註】「be＋不定詞」用於第一人稱疑問句時，表示徵求、請教對方的意思。

What **am I to do**?（我該做什麼？）

= What do you want me to do?

② **seem, appear, prove, turn out**… ＋ 不定詞

跟隨在此類動詞之後的不定詞是用來作爲主詞補語。"…to be…" 的形式可以省略，意義不變。可以用「It＋V＋that 子句」的句型來代換。

He seems (to be) ill.（他似乎生病了。）

= It seems that he is ill.

The man turned out (to be) an impostor.（這人結果是個騙子。）

The report proved (to be) true.（這個報告已證明是眞的。）

He appears (to be) very young.（他看起來很年輕。）

3. 作副詞用：

⑴ 修飾動詞

① 表目的（to ＝ in order to）

不定詞片語當副詞用修飾動詞表目的

He works hard *to keep* *his family in comfort*.（他努力工作使家人生活舒適。）

（= He works hard (in order) that he may keep his family in comfort.）

We go to school *to study*.（我們到學校唸書。）

I keep a dog *to watch* *my house*.（我養一隻狗看家。）

We eat *to live*, (but do) not live *to eat*.（我們吃飯爲活著，不是活著爲吃飯。）

【註】爲了加強語氣可用 **in order to**。

爲表帶有結果或必有結果的目的則用 **so as to**。如：

He works hard day and night *in order to* (*or so as to*) pass the entrance examination next year.

（他日以繼夜地用功是爲了能通過明年的入學考試。）

In order to secure a good seat, you'll have to get there before eight.

（想要得到好的座位，你必須在八點以前到那裡。）

再則表目的的不定詞（不論有無 "in order"）可置於句首以示加強語氣，但句子的主詞必須是該不定詞的意義主詞。如：

In order to appreciate poetry, *it* should be read aloud.【誤】

In order to appreciate poetry, *you* should read it aloud.【正】

（爲了要欣賞詩，應該出聲朗誦。）

【主要動詞的主詞，也是不定詞意義上的主詞，根據句意一定是 you，而不是 it 在欣賞詩】

To be a good citizen, *obeying the law* is necessary.【誤】

To be a good citizen, *one* must obey the law.【正】

（要想做個好公民，必須要守法。）

【obeying the law 怎能做 to be a good citizen 的意義上的主詞？！】

② **表結果**

不定詞片語當副詞用修飾動詞表結果

He grew up *to be* a famous scholar. (他長大之後成了有名的學者。)

(= When he grew up, he became a famous scholar.)

I opened the door *to find* the room empty. (我把門打開，結果發現房間是空的。)

(= I opened the door and found the room empty.)

【註】表「令人失望的結果」用 **only to**…；表「結果沒有再」用 **never to**…。

He worked hard *only to fail*. (他很努力，結果卻失敗。)

He accumulated an enormous sum of money *only to die* before long.

(他累積了一大筆錢，但不久就死了。)

They parted, *never to see* each other again. (他們分開了，從此沒有再見面。)

The good old days are past, *never to return* to us again.

(舊日的美好時光過去了，永遠不會再回來了。)

③ **表原因**：大部分為感情的原因。

不定詞片語當副詞用修飾動詞表原因

I wondered *to hear* her voice in the next room. (我因聽見隔壁房間有她的聲音而感到奇怪。)

(= I wondered because I heard her voice in the next room.)

I grieve *to learn* of your conduct. (我因得知你的行為而感到難過。)

She wept *to see* him in that condition. (她看到他如此處境而落淚。)

I could not but laugh *to hear* such a funny story. (我聽到如此滑稽的故事不禁大笑起來。)

He rejoiced *to know* that she was still alive. (他因為得知她還活著所以很高興。)

They rejoiced *to know* that he would come soon. (他們因為得知他很快就回來，都很高興。)

④ **表理由**：大部分是推斷的理由。

不定詞片語當副詞用修飾動詞表理由

He must be a fool *to say so*. (他說這種話，一定是個傻瓜。)

(= He must be a fool, for he says so.)

He must be rich *to buy that car*. (他買那部車，一定很有錢。)

He must have studied hard *to have succeeded* so splendidly.

(他有如此輝煌的成就，他一定曾經苦學過。)

What a lucky fellow I was *to have* such an income. (我有如此的收入，真是個幸運兒。)

You are no gentleman *to hit* a lady in the face. (你打女人耳光，實在不是個紳士。)

⑤ **表條件**

不定詞片語當副詞用修飾動詞表條件

You would make a great mistake *to take his bribe*. (你如果接受他的賄賂，你就犯了大錯。)

(= You would make a great mistake if you took his bribe.)

I should be happy *to be* of any service to you. (如果我能幫助你，我會非常高興。)

(= If I am of any service to you, I should be happy.)

It would be difficult *to find* a teacher better than our former one.

(= It would be difficult if we tried to find a teacher better than our former one.)

(我們要想找個比以前那位更好的老師，真的很難。)

To hear him _talk_, you would take him for a scholar.

（= If you heard him talk, you would take him for a scholar.）

（如果你聽了他的談話，你會認爲他是個學者。）

It would take up too much time **_to tell_** you _the whole story_.

（= It would take up too much time if I were to tell you the whole story.）

（假如我告訴你全部的情形，會花很多時間。）

⑥ 代替「**that + 主詞 + should…**」子句。表示主要子句裡責難和批評的理由。

What a fool I was **_to trust him_**!（我竟然信任他，我眞是個傻瓜！）
= What a fool I was _that I should trust him_!

How stupid of you **_to go there_**!（你竟然去那裡，眞是愚蠢！）
= How stupid of you _that you should go there_!

⑵ **修飾形容詞**：修飾形容詞的不定詞必須置於被修飾的形容詞之後。

The question is difficult **_to answer_**.（這問題很難回答。）

This mushroom is good **_to eat_**.（這蘑菇很好吃。）

It is not fit **_to drink_** (_or to be drunk_).（這不適合飲用。）【fit 之後可接主動和被動的不定詞】

It is likely **_to rain_**.（可能會下雨。）

Only human beings are able **_to laugh_**.（只有人類才會笑。）

She is eager **_to learn_** _to speak English_.（她很想學說英語。）

He is apt **_to get_** _angry_.（他容易生氣。）

I am not competent **_to judge_**.（我無法判斷。）

Everybody was anxious **_to know_** _what had happened_.（每個人都急著想知道發生了什麼事。）

I am curious **_to hear_** _the story_.（我很想聽這個故事。）

She is dying **_to see_** _him_.（她很想見他。）

I am willing **_to cooperate_** _with you_.（我願意跟你合作。）

Be sure **_to come_** _at five this evening_.（今天傍晚五點一定要來。）

You are mad **_to go_** _in this weather_.（這樣的天氣你要去，眞是瘋了。）

She was lucky **_to escape_** _being hurt_.（她眞幸運沒有受傷。）

My parents will be delighted (pleased, happy, glad) **_to see you_**.（我的父母會很高興見到你。）

⑶ **修飾副詞**

① **too + 形容詞或副詞 + to~**「太…而不能；太…沒有…」這一句型中的不定詞是用來修飾副詞 too，表否定的結果。

I was **_too_** tired **_to walk_** _any farther_.（我太疲倦，不能再走更遠了。）

It is **_never_** too late **_to mend_**.（亡羊補牢，猶未晚也。）

Nothing is too difficult **_to be conquered_** _by perseverance_.

（沒有什麼事情是難到不能用毅力克服的。）

The artificial flowers are too skillfully made *to be distinguished* *from natural ones*.

（這些人造花做得太巧妙了，和天然的花沒有分別。）

【註1】**too ready to～ 句型中的不定詞是用來修飾 ready 的**，而不是修飾 too，該不定詞也**沒有否定的意味。**屬於像 ready 這類的形容詞還有 **apt, eager, willing, inclined, easy** 等，都是「很喜歡…」之意。此種用法可看成 too…to 的例外。

He is too ready to criticize others. （他很喜歡批評別人。）
= He is very fond of criticizing others.

She is too ready to suspect. （她疑心病太重。）
= She is very fond of suspecting.

【註2】**only** (*or* **all**, **but**, **really**) **too** = **very** 後如接不定詞時，是修飾前面的形容詞，而不是修飾 too，該不定詞當然沒有否定意味。此種用法可看成 too…to 的例外。

I am only too glad to see you. （見到你我非常高興。）
= I am very glad to see you.
You are really too kind. （你真是仁慈。）
= You are very kind.
The play ended all (*or* but) too soon. （這場戲結束得太快。）

【註3】"**too…for** + （動）名詞" 和 "**too…to**" 的意思相同。但 too…for 接動名詞時不可用被動語態，也不可用所有格。

These grapes are too sour for eating. （這些葡萄太酸，不能吃。）
= These grapes are too sour to eat.
These grapes are too sour for *being eaten*. 【誤】
These grapes are too sour for *my* eating. 【誤】
My emotion is too great for words. （我激動得說不出話。）
It is too difficult for a textbook. （這太難了，不能做教科書。）

【註4】"**too…not to～**" 是雙重否定，意思是「非常…不會不…」。
He is too wise not to see that. （他很聰明不會不明白那一點。）

【註5】**never** (**not**) **too…to～** 的意思是「不會太…而不能（會）」。
One is never too old to learn. （活到老學到老。）
It is not (yet) too late for him to go there. （他這時候到那裡還不會太遲。）

【註6】**can not…too～** 是「再怎麼…都不嫌太過份；無論怎樣…都不為過」之意。
We can not admire her beauty too much. （我們怎麼讚美她的美麗都不為過。）
One can not be too faithful to one's duties. （對職務再怎麼忠實都是不過份的。）

【註7】**none too** = **not at all too** 是「一點也不」之意。
We were none too early for the plane. （我們剛好趕上飛機。）

② **so** + 形容詞或副詞 + **as to～** 「非常…所以；如此…以致於」不定詞 as to～是用來修飾副詞 so，表前面原因的結果。

She is *so* young *as to look* *quite like a child*. （她很年輕，看起來很像小孩子。）

= She is *so* young *that she looks quite like a child*.

He spoke *so* eloquently *as to move* us to tears.（他口才太好，使我們感動得落淚。）

= He spoke *so* eloquently *that he moved us to tears.*

The mother worried *so* much about her son's safety *as to be* unable to sleep all night.

= The mother worried *so* much about her son's safety *that she couldn't sleep all night.*
（這母親非常擔心她兒子的安全，以致整夜不能入睡。）

【註】　在 such + 名詞 + as to～句型中，such 是形容詞修飾後面的名詞；在 such as to～
中，such = so great，不定詞 as to～用來修飾形容詞 such。

I am not *such* a fool *as to believe* that.（我不是一個傻瓜會相信那個。）

His progress was <u>*such* as to surprise</u> his teacher.
　　　　　　　　　　＝
　　　　　　　　　so great
（他的進步很大，以致使他的老師感到驚訝。）

③ **enough to～**「足以」這一句型中的不定詞是修飾副詞 enough 表結果。

She was kind enough *to lend* me the money.（她很仁慈，肯把錢借給我。）

You are old enough *to understand* what I say.（你年紀夠大，應該了解我所說的。）

I don't know him well enough *to lend* him the money.（我還不夠了解他，不能借錢給他。）

4. **不定詞的獨立用法**：不定詞有時與其它部分沒有文法關聯，而獨立存在，稱為**獨立不定詞**，
也可說是副詞片語修飾全句。常見的獨立不定詞如下：

to { tell / speak / say } the truth	(I am) glad to say（說來很高興）
	(I am) sorry to say（說來很難過）
to speak { frankly / sincerely } （老實說；坦白說）	(It is) sad to say（說也可悲）
	(It is) needless to say（不用說）
to be { plain / candid / frank } with you	(It is) strange to say（說也奇怪）
	not to say（雖然不能說）
to confess the truth	so to speak (*or* say)（可以說是）
	to begin (*or* start) with（首先）
to make a long story short	to do him justice（公平地說）
to cut a long story short	to be sure（的確；當然）
to make the story short	to pass to another subject（換個話題）
to make short of a long story （簡單地說）	to say nothing of…
to sum up	not to speak of…
to be brief	not to mention… （更不用說）
	let alone…
to make matters (*or* things) worse（更糟的是）	
to return to the subject (*or* our mutton)	
to take (*or* pick) up the thread of the story （言歸正傳）	
to resume the thread of the story (*or* one's discourse)	

To tell the truth, I have no money with me.（坦白說，我身上沒帶錢。）

Strange to say, his hair turned white during the night.
（說也奇怪，他的頭髮一夜之間變白了。）

To do him justice, we must say that he is generous.
（公平而論，我們應該說他是慷慨的。）

To begin with, he can't speak English.（第一，他不會說英語。）

For the time being he is unemployed, and *to make matters worse*, his wife is in the hospital.（目前他失業了，更糟的是，他太太在住院。）

To make a long story short, his project ended in a failure.
（長話短說，他的計劃最後失敗了。）

To confess the truth, she was remarkably plain.（坦白說，她實在不漂亮。）

He owns much property in New York, *not to mention* a large summer estate in Connecticut.（他在紐約有很多的財產，更不用說他在康州還有一大棟夏季別墅呢。）

5. **不定詞的其他用法：**

⑴ **疑問詞 + 不定詞 = 名詞片語**，此片語是由表「義務」的名詞子句簡化而來。

How to do it is the problem.（如何做是個問題。）
= *How it should be done* is the problem.

Ask her *how to write this word correctly*.（問她怎麼寫這個字才正確。）
= Ask her *how this word must be written correctly*.

⑵ **介詞 + whom（或 which）+ 不定詞 = 形容詞片語**，此形容詞片語是形容詞子句簡化而來。

The poor man has no house *in which he can live*.（那窮人沒有房子住。）
　　　　　　　　　　→ *in which to live*.【前後主詞相同才可簡化，in 不可放在 live 後】
　　　　　　　　　　→ *to live in*.【再簡化時把關代去掉，in 一定要放在 live 後】

I want some money *with which I can buy a book*.（我需要錢買一本書。）
　　　　　　　　　　→ *with which to buy a book*.
　　　　　　　　　　→ *to buy a book with*.

⑶ **不定詞片語可代替祈使句或感嘆句。**

Oh, to be a boy again!（噢，要是我再回到小時候該有多好！）
= Oh, *how I wish I might be a boy again*!

To think of that man having the impudence to call!
= *How I hate to think of that man having the impudence to call!*
（我不願想那個人厚著臉皮打電話給我！）

⑷ **原形不定詞的慣用表達法：**

① had $\left\{ \begin{matrix} \text{better} \\ \text{best} \end{matrix} \right\}$ + 原形不定詞，作「最好」解

You *had better* (or *best*) *do* it yourself.（你最好自己做。）
You *had better give* up smoking.（你最好戒煙。）
You *had better* not *go* shopping on such a hot day.
（在如此炎熱的天氣，你最好不要去逛街。）

② $\left.\begin{array}{l}\text{cannot but}\\\text{cannot help but}\\\text{cannot choose but}\end{array}\right\}$ + 原形不定詞，作「不得不」解

= cannot help + 動名詞

I *cannot but* think so. (我不得不這麼想。)

= I *cannot help but* think so.

= I *cannot choose but* think so.

= I *cannot help* thinking so.

【註】can but + 原形不定詞中，but = only

　　　I can *but* listen. (我只能聽聽罷了。)

　　　I can *but* lose the salary. (我至多不過損失薪水罷了。)

③ $\left.\begin{array}{l}\text{would (had)}\left\{\begin{array}{l}\text{rather}\\\text{sooner}\end{array}\right\}\text{+ 原形不定詞}\cdots\text{+ than}\\\text{would (had) as soon + 原形不定詞}\cdots\text{+ as}\end{array}\right\}$ + 原形不定詞，

作「寧願⋯而不願；與其⋯不如」解

I *would rather stay* home tonight. (今晚我寧願待在家裡。)

I *had rather die than live* in dishonor. (我寧可死也不願苟且偷生。)

I *had sooner go* out in the rain *than stay* indoors. (我寧願出去淋雨，也不願待在屋子裡。)

【註】than 或 as 後的原形動詞與前面相同時可省略。

　　　I *would as soon go* there *as* (*go*) anywhere.

④ do nothing (*or* ⋯not do anything) but (*or* except) + 原形不定詞，作「只」解

She *did nothing but* weep. (她只是哭。)

You *have nothing to do but* wait. (你只有等待。)

We *had done nothing except* send for a doctor. (我們除了去請醫生之外，什麼事也沒有做。)

⑤ Better + 原形不定詞，作「還是⋯好」解，是 "It would be better to~" 及 "⋯had better + 原形不定詞" 的省略表達法

Better leave it undone. (還是不要做比較好。)

= *It would be better to leave it undone.*

= *You had better leave it undone.*

Better bend than break. (【諺】寧屈不斷；大丈夫能屈能伸。)

⑥ All one has to do is + 原形不定詞，常見於美式英語中 (參照 p.648)

All I have to do is take a rest. (我所必須要做的就是休息。)

If you want to see some beautiful paintings, *all you have to do is* go to this art museum.

(如果你要看一些美麗的畫，你只要去這間美術館就可看到。)

⑦ **come**, **go** 作為命令句或祈使句，可接原形不定詞，常見於美式英語

I'll *go tell* the young lady.【實際上是由 go 後面的 and 或 to 省略而來】

= I'll *go and tell* the young lady.

= I'll *go to tell* the young lady. (我要去告訴那位小姐。)

John, *go paint* the fence! (約翰，去油漆籬笆！)

Henry, *come join* the picnic tomorrow. (亨利，明天來參加野餐。)

VII. 不定詞用法上應注意事項：

1. **感官動詞之後**，用原形動詞做受詞補語，常用的感官動詞有：see, hear, feel, watch, behold, perceive（感覺）, observe（察覺）, notice（注意到）, overhear（偷聽）, listen to, look at 等。

Look at it *snow* now!（你看，正在下雪！）
We *listened to* the band *play* in the park.（我們在公園裡聽樂隊演奏。）
I *watched* him *go*.（我看到他走。）
Did you *feel* the house *shake*?（你感覺到房子在震動嗎？）
I *hear* a bird *sing*.（我聽到鳥叫。）
I *observed* her *turn* pale.（我察覺到她臉色變得蒼白。）

【註 1】 hear 可省略它的受詞 *people*（*someone*），直接接 say, speak, tell, talk 等動詞。
I *hear*（*people*）*say* that there will be an election soon.
（我聽說不久將會有選舉。）

【註 2】 一般說來，在感官動詞之後的原形不定詞與現在分詞可以互換，不致影響意義太大。但有時原形動詞強調其動作的事實，而現在分詞則強調正在進行的一瞬間。**特意看到或聽到用原形不定詞；無意中看到或聽到用現在分詞。**

I saw him *drink* wine.（我看過他喝酒。）
I saw him *drinking* wine.（我看到他正在喝酒。）

I felt the car *move*.（我感到車子動了。）
I felt the car *moving*.（我感到車子正在動。）

I made it a rule to hear her *sing*.【正】 *singing*.【誤】（我習慣聽她唱歌。）

Last night when I passed her room, I heard her *singing*.【正】 *sing*.【誤】
（昨晚當我經過她的房間時，聽見她在唱歌。）

【註 3】 在被動語態中，感官動詞後面的不定詞的 to 就不能省略，如：
I saw him *enter* the room.（我看到他走進房間。）
= He was seen *to enter* the room.（他被看到走進房間。）

【註 4】 感官動詞 **see, feel** 若當「**知道**」解並以 **to be** 為受詞補語時，**不可省略 to**。
We *see* it *to be* so even in the case of aged people.【see = understand】
（我們了解即使老年人也是如此。）
He *felt* the plan *to be* unwise.【felt = was of the opinion】
（他覺得該計劃不明智。）

2. **使役動詞之後**，要用原形不定詞做受詞補語。
Let him *go*.（讓他走。）
Leave it *be*.（順其自然。）
= Let it *be*.

I must have someone *repair* my shoes.（我必須找個人修鞋子。）

Bid the fellow *wait*.（叫那傢伙等一等。）

但 Money makes the mare *(to) go*.（有錢能使鬼推磨。）── 此格言裡 to 省略或保留均可。

【註1】　使役動詞如：**let**, **make**, **have**, **bid** 等四個字後接原形不定詞，其他使役動詞如：cause, compel, order, force, oblige, persuade, urge 等其後仍接有 **to 之不定詞**，而 help 則接原形不定詞與帶 to 的不定詞皆可。但被動語態的使役動詞後，to 不可省。

（詳見 p.381）

He *compelled* me *to do* such a thing.（他強迫我做這種事。）

I *caused* the boy *to get* up early.（我叫那男孩早起。）

(= I had the boy get up early.)

　　　She *helped* mother *prepare* for Christmas.（她幫助母親準備過聖誕節。）
　　　It *helps* no one *to understand*.（它不能使任何人明白。）

【註2】　have, get 和 make 等字受詞後的被動語態不定詞裡，be 或 to be 要省略。

Please have my room *painted*.（請油漆我的房間。）

I must get it *done*.（我必須叫人把它完成。）

He could not make himself *understood*.（他無法使別人了解他的意思。）

但是 let, **bid** 和其他的使役動詞受詞後的被動語態不定詞裡的 **be 或 to be 不可省略**。

Let him *be* punished at once.（讓他立刻受處罰。）

I must *bid* the door *be* painted.（我必須請人油漆這扇門。）

He *caused* the tuition *to be* paid.（他叫我們付學費。）

3. 不定詞中的原形動詞與前面的動詞重複時，不定詞**只要用 to 代表**即可。

A: Will you go with me?（你要和我一起去嗎？）

B: I am glad *to* (*go with you*).〔我很願意（和你一起去）。〕

I meant *to do* it, but forgot *to*.（我是想去做，但忘了。）

I meant *to destroy* it from the first, but I was afraid *to*.

（我一開始就想摧毀它，但是我不敢。）

4. **並列的數個不定詞，to 的省略與保留**

⑴ 由對等連接詞 and 或 or 連接作用相同的不定詞時，只保留第一個不定詞裡的 to。

I wrote this letter in order *to persuade* and *encourage* Mary.
（我寫這封信是為了說服並鼓勵瑪麗。）

I didn't know whether *to sit* or *stand*.（我不知道是要坐還是站。）

⑵ 為了**對比**或**強調**，或為表示**平衡**時，每一個不定詞的 **to 都要保留**。

I came *to praise* him, (but) not *to blame* him.
（我來讚美他，不是來責備他的。）

It will take months *to raise* the money, *to erect* the building, *to install* the machinery, *to buy* enough raw material, and then *to start* work.
（籌募款項、建造房屋、安裝機器、購買足夠的原料，然後開工，要花好幾個月的時間。）

⑶ 數個不定詞由連接詞連接，前者無 to 時，後者也必須省略；前者有 to 時，後者可有可無。

I can *do* nothing but *laugh*. (我只能笑笑。)

He came to see me so as *to persuade* and (*to*) *encourage* me.

(他來看我爲了要說服我和鼓勵我。)

It is easier *to say* something than (*to*) *do* it. (說比做容易。)

I advised him *to be* honest and (*to*) *work* harder.

(我勸他要誠實，並要更努力工作。)

5. **不定詞之修飾語及其位置**：副詞修飾不定詞，其位置有下列三種：

⑴ **置於不定詞之後**，通常是描述性的副詞

I want him to write his address *correctly* and *clearly*.

(我要他把住址寫正確，而且清楚。)

He was ordered to go to school *punctually*. (他奉命準時上學。)

⑵ **置於不定詞之前**，通常爲表示否定的副詞

I advised him *never* to go to such a place. (我勸他絕不可到那種地方去。)

Before she went out, she put on a coat in order *not* to catch cold.

(出去之前，她穿上外套以免感冒。)

It is better *never* to mind what cannot be prevented.

(最好不要把不可挽回的事放在心上。)

【例外】*Early* to bed and *early* to rise makes a man healthy.

(早睡早起使人健康。)

⑶ **置於不定詞之間**（即**分離不定詞**），爲表示特別加強用法，或爲避免句意含糊時才使用。比較下面句子：

She wishes *entirely to forget* her past. ——【句意不清】

【entirely 可修飾 wishes，也可修飾 to forget，因此容易引起誤解】

⎰ She wishes *to forget* her past *entirely*.【entirely 修飾 to forget】
⎱ She wishes *to entirely forget* her past.【entirely 修飾 forget 比上句強】
　 (她希望完全忘掉她的過去。)

⎰ It is difficult *to understand* this point *clearly*.【一般情形】
⎱ It is difficult *to clearly understand* this point.【加強語氣】
　 (要清楚地了解這一點是困難的。)

再看下面的例句：

It is difficult for a son *to always live up to* the expectations of his parents.

(要兒子永遠達到父母的期望是困難的。)

We must expect the Commission *to at least neglect* our interests.

(我們必須預期到該委員會至少會忽視我們的利益。)

He was strong enough *to really climb* the mountain alone.

(他強壯得足以眞正地自己單獨攀登此山。)

VIII. 不定詞的時式：

1. **簡單式不定詞**

⑴ 表示與主要動詞同時間的動作或狀況

> He *seems to be* tired.（他似乎累了。）
> = It *seems* that he *is* tired.

> He *seemed to be* tired.（他似乎累了。）
> = It *seemed* that he *was* tired.

> He *is said to be* very rich.（據說他非常富有。）
> = It *is said* that he *is* very rich.

> He *was believed to be* honest.（人們相信他是誠實的。）
> = It *was believed* that he *was* honest.

⑵ 表示發生在主要動詞之後的動作，像未來的願望、期待等，此種用法的動詞常用的有：promise, wish, hope, expect, plan, want, mean, intend…等。

> We *expect* him *to come*.（我們希望他會來。）
> = We *expect* that he *will come*.

> We *expected* him *to come*.（我們期待過他會來。）
> = We *expected* that he *would come*.

> She *promises to write* to me once a week.（她答應每週給我寫封信。）
> = She *says* (that) she *will write* to me once a week.

> She *promised to write* to me once a week.（她答應過每週給我寫封信。）
> = She *said* (that) she *would write* to me once a week.

2. **完成式不定詞**

⑴ 表示發生在主要動詞之前的動作

> He *seems to have been* ill.（他似乎曾生過病。）
> = It *seems* that he *was* (or *has been*) ill.

> He *seemed to have been* ill.（他似乎生過病。）
> = It *seemed* that he *had been* ill.

> He *is said to have been* rich.（據說他曾經富有過。）
> = It *is said* that he *was* (or *had been*) rich.

> He *was said to have been* rich.（據說他從前曾經富有過。）
> = It *was said* that he *had been* rich.

⑵ 表過去沒有實現的願望、期待或計劃，可用表希望、計劃等動詞的過去式加上完成式的不定詞形式表達。

wished, hoped, intended, meant, expected, planned promised, wanted, thought, desired, were, was would like, should like	+ to have + p.p.

I wished *to have bought* a car, but I had no money.
〔我希望買部車，但我（當時）沒有錢。〕

I intended *to have come*. (我本打算來的。── 但沒來)

I intended *to have gone* abroad that year, but my mother suddenly fell sick.

(我打算那年出國，但那時我母親突然生病了。)

He meant *to have come* to see you last night but the city was unexpectedly placed under martial law.

(昨晚他有意來看你，但卻沒想到城裡戒嚴了。)

【註 1】 上述完成式不定詞可以用簡單式代替，但後面必須有其他詞語表示動作沒有實現。

He hoped *to pass* the examination. 【句意不清，未說明通過考試沒有】
He hoped *to have passed* the examination. 【正】

(他原本希望通過考試。── 可是沒通過)

He hoped $\begin{Bmatrix} \textit{to have passed} 【正】 \\ \textit{to pass} 【正】 \end{Bmatrix}$ the examination, but failed.

(他希望通過考試，但是失敗了。)

【註 2】 現代英語也用前述動詞的完成式表示過去未實現的願望。(參照 p.338, 339)

I *had meant* to do so. (我原本打算這樣做的。)

3. 進行式不定詞

   ⑴ 表示主要動詞的動作發生時，**正在持續中的動作**，有強調的作用。

   He seems *to be working* very hard. (他似乎很努力地在工作。)
   I discovered him *to be eating* in the room. (我發現他在房間裡吃東西。)

   ⑵ 在主要動詞之後，表示**即刻的未來**。

   The old man seems *to be dying*. (這老人似乎要死了。)

4. 完成進行式不定詞：表自過去某時開始的動作或狀態，一直持續到主要動詞所表示的時間時，仍在進行或繼續，或剛剛停止。

   You seem *to have been writing* very long. (你好像已經寫了很久了。)

IX. 不定詞的語態及其用法：

1. **當名詞用的不定詞，其語態的主動或被動依照其含義而決定。**

   Do you want *to teach* such a child? (你要教像那樣的小孩嗎？)
   Do you want *to be taught* French? (你想要請人教你法文嗎？)

   His father seems *to misunderstand* him. (他父親似乎誤會他了。)
   He seems *to be misunderstood* by his father. (他似乎被他父親誤會了。)

   He likes *to speak* ill of others. (他喜歡說別人壞話。)
   Nobody likes *to be spoken* ill of. (沒有人喜歡被人說壞話。)

   To love and *to be loved* is the greatest happiness on earth.

   (愛人而且被愛是世界上最幸福的事。)

【例外】 **to blame**, **to let**（出租）, **to do** 當主詞補語時，常以主動形式表被動的意思。

I am *to blame*（= to be blamed）.（都是我不好。）

Much remains *to do*（= to be done）.（還有許多事要做。）

This house is *to let*.（此屋出租。）

※ **let** 當「**出租**」解時，較少用被動式，但若有副詞修飾語，或另一不定詞做對照時，則可用被動式。

This house is *to be let* for six hundred dollars a month.

（這房子每月租金 600 元。）

This boat is *to be let*, not *to be sold*.（這艘船是出租，不是要賣的。）

2. **當形容詞的不定詞，通常用主動語態。為表示強調時，可用被動語態。**

I have no chair *to sit* on.（我沒有椅子可坐。）

A black tie was the proper thing *to wear*.（黑領帶是適合穿戴的東西。）

She has a lot of letters *to write*.（她有許多信要寫。）

There is nothing *to fear*（*to be feared*）.（沒有什麼好怕的。）

There is only one thing *to do*（*to be done*）.（只有一件事要做。）

There is no house *to let*（*to be let*）.（沒有房子出租。）

【註】 當形容詞用的不定詞，有時因語態不同，意義也會有不同。

There are many beautiful animals *to see*（= *worth seeing*）in the zoo.

（動物園裡有很多美麗的動物值得一看。）

There are many beautiful animals *to be seen*（= *that can be seen*）in the zoo.

（動物園裡可以看到許多美麗的動物。）

3. **當副詞用的不定詞，都用主動語態。**

The questions are hard $\begin{cases} \textit{to understand}. 【正】 \\ \textit{to be understood}. 【誤】 \end{cases}$（這些問題很難了解。）

He is not easy *to get* along with.（他不容易相處。）

The apartment is large enough *to live in*.（這個公寓住起來夠大。）

【註】 若受程度副詞如 too…to 所限制，或含必定、必然性之意，則可用被動語態表示被動意義。

He spoke in a voice too low *to be heard*.（他說話的聲音太低，聽不見。）

He is too young *to be sent* to America for advanced study.

（他太年輕，不能送到美國去深造。）

He is sure *to be promoted*.（他一定會升遷。）

第二章 動名詞（Gerunds）

I. 定義： **動名詞是有名詞的性質**，在句中可做主詞、受詞等，**又有動詞的性質**，可以帶有受詞、補語，或由副詞（片語）等修飾。

II. 形式：

時式 ＼ 語態	主　動　語　態	被　動　語　態
簡　單　式	原形動詞 + ing writing	being + 過去分詞 being written
完　成　式	having + 過去分詞 having written	having been + 過去分詞 having been written

III. 動名詞意義上的主詞：

1. **在下列情形下，動名詞不須再表明意義上的主詞。**

   (1) 一些眾所周知的事

   Eating too much makes one fat. （吃太多會使人發胖。）
   Flying by night is considered perfectly safe nowadays.
   （夜間飛行現在被認為是很安全的。）

   (2) 當動名詞的意義主詞與主要動詞的主詞或受詞相同，或由上下文可以推斷其意義主詞時

   John likes *going* to the cinema once a week. （約翰喜歡每週去看一次電影。）
   【主詞 John 是 going 的意義主詞】

   She blamed *him* for *doing* such a thing. （她責備他做這種事。）
   【受詞 him 是 doing 的意義主詞】

   She is proud of *being* rich. （她以富有感到驕傲。）
   【主詞 She 是 being 的意義主詞】

   The pain in *my* throat makes *speaking* quite impossible. （喉嚨的痛使得我無法講話。）
   【speaking 的意義主詞由 my throat 可以推測為 "I"】

2. **動名詞的意義主詞，與句子的主詞或受詞不同時，則須表示出來。**

   (1) **生物名詞要用 's 的形式表示**

   John's coming home tomorrow excites all of us. （約翰明日要回家，使我們都很興奮。）

   【註】（代）名詞當主詞時，必須用所有格。當受詞時則可用所有格，也可用受格。

   Mary【誤】
   Mary's【正】 } being diligent cannot be denied. （瑪麗很勤勉是不容否認的。）

   I am sure of my { *brother's*【正】
   brother【正】 } passing the examination.
   （我確信我弟弟會通過考試。）

   There is little chance of { *his*【正】
   him【正】 } being ejected. （他被驅逐的機會很小。）

(2) 無生物的名詞或抽象名詞，照原來形式不必加 's

We must allow for the ***train being*** late. (我們必須考慮火車的延誤。)

I am glad of the ***examination being*** over. (我很高興考試結束了。)

I am sure of the ***news being*** true. (我確信消息是正確的。)

(3) 代名詞則用所有格形式

Mother hates ***our playing*** indoors. (母親討厭我們在屋內玩。)

It is no use ***your trying*** to cheat me. (你想欺騙我是沒有用的。)

IV. 動名詞的性質及用法：

1. 名詞的性質

(1) 做主詞

Swimming is good for the health. (游泳對健康有益。)

Blushing is a sign of modesty. (臉紅是謙虛的表徵。)

Raising your hat to a lady is good manners. (對一位女士脫帽致意是好的禮貌。)

Parking is prohibited on this street. (這條街上禁止停車。)

It is no use ***crying*** over spilt milk. (覆水難收。)【It 為虛主詞】

(2) 做受詞

He enjoys ***camping*** in the mountains. (他喜歡在山中露營。)

We would appreciate ***hearing*** from you. (我們會感謝你的來信。)

He denied ***taking*** the key. (他否認拿那鑰匙。)

He earns his living by ***selling*** brushes. (他以賣刷子維生。)

In ***taking*** the cake out of the oven, I burned my hand. (在拿蛋糕出烤箱時，我燙了手。)

The child was saved from ***drowning*** by the lifeguard. (小孩被救生員救起，免於淹死。)

He objected to ***going*** there. (他反對去那裡。)

I am accustomed to ***working*** late. (我習慣於工作到很晚。)

I am tired of ***arguing*** with you all the time. (我討厭老是和你爭論。)

He is past ***praying*** for. (= He is beyond being prayed for.) (他是無藥可救的。)

(3) 做補語

Teaching is ***learning***. (教學相長。)

My hobby is ***making*** model airplanes. (我的嗜好是做模型飛機。)

His favorite sport is ***swimming***. (他所喜歡的運動是游泳。)

【注意】 因為現在分詞與動名詞的形式一樣，所以要留心不要弄混淆，<u>請比較下面兩句</u>：

He is ***singing*** now. (他現在正在唱歌。)【singing 是現在分詞和 is 做成進行式】

His hobby is ***singing***. (他的嗜好是唱歌。)

【singing 是動名詞，是主詞補語，如果是分詞，豈不變成他的 hobby 正在唱歌！】

(4) 做同位語

This is my recreation, ***reading novels***. (這便是我的娛樂，看小說。)

His hobby, ***making model airplanes***, is very interesting.

(他做模型飛機的嗜好，非常有趣。)

⑸ **做形容詞**：名詞可以修飾名詞，動名詞和名詞一樣可作形容詞用修飾名詞，表示該名詞的功用。

a *dancing* teacher（舞蹈老師）　　a *writing* desk（書桌）

a *smoking* room（吸煙室）　　*drinking* water（飲用水）

a *walking* stick（手杖）

⑹ **動名詞之前可加冠詞或所有格形容詞**

I considered *the taking* of every fish as a kind of murder.

（我認爲捕盡所有的魚是一種謀殺的行爲。）

A knocking at the door was heard.（我聽到敲門聲。）

I told her the reason for *my doubting*.（我告訴她我懷疑的理由。）

⑺ **動名詞之前也可加形容詞**

They did a lot of *loud arguing* last night.（昨晚他們大聲地爭吵。）

There is *no saying* what may happen.（會發生什麼事很難說。）

2. **動詞的性質**

⑴ **動名詞後面可接受詞**

After *reading the novel* I went to bed.（看完小說，我就上床睡覺。）

Most of the children like *playing baseball*.（大多數的小孩喜歡打棒球。）

He was grateful for our *attending his graduation*.（他感激我們參加他的畢業典禮。）

⑵ **動名詞後面可接補語**

Being idle is the cause of his failure.（懶惰是他失敗的原因。）

Instead of *becoming cheerful*, he became rather sad.（他沒變得快樂，而是相當悲傷。）

⑶ **可有副詞修飾**

Working so *hard* will produce good results.（這麼努力地工作會產生好的結果。）

He enjoyed *swimming in the lake*.（他喜歡在湖裡游泳。）

Would you mind *speaking* more *slowly*?（你介意說慢一點嗎？）

⑷ **可有完成式**

Excuse me for *not having answered* your letter at once.（原諒我沒有立刻給你回信。）

They all thanked him for *having done* it.（他們都感謝他做了那件事。）

⑸ **可有被動語態**

I don't like *being treated* like that.（我不喜歡受到那樣的對待。）

I don't like *being disturbed* while studying.（我唸書時不喜歡被打擾。）

3. **動名詞形的名詞**：有些名詞和動名詞形式一樣（字尾加 ing），但在用法上是純粹的名詞，同樣一個 ~ing 字，有時是動名詞，有時已經完全名詞化，用法和名詞一樣，有複數形和所有格。

A proper *beginning* makes a proper end.（好的開始就會有好的結束。）
　　　　　　純粹名詞

Beginning such a job is not easy.（開始做那樣的工作是不容易的。）
動名詞當主詞

The ***shooting*** of birds is forbidden.（射鳥是被禁止的。）
　　　純粹名詞

Shooting birds is useless.（射鳥是沒有用的。）
動名詞當主詞

下面例句裡的動名詞已經完全名詞化，成為純粹名詞。

I don't like reading for ***reading's*** sake（= for the sake of reading）.
（我不喜歡只為讀書而讀書。）

I cannot understand his recent ***sayings*** and ***doings***.（我不能了解他最近的言行。）

【註】　常見的動名詞形的純粹名詞如下：（實際上動名詞形的名詞有無數個）

① 當**抽象名詞**用的動名詞形名詞

accounting（會計學）	living（生活）	learning（學識）
swimming（游泳）	sightseeing（觀光）	feeling（感覺）
fishing（釣魚）	saving（儲蓄）	ending（結局）
beginning（開始）	blessing（祝福）	shooting（射擊；狩獵）

② 當**普通名詞**用的動名詞形名詞，可有單、複數形式

writing(s)（文章）	reading(s)（讀物）	building(s)（建築物）
meaning(s)（意義）	meeting(s)（會議）	saying(s)（諺語）
drawing(s)（圖畫）	warning(s)（警告）	painting(s)（畫）

③ 常以**複數形式**出現的動名詞形名詞

surroundings（環境）	tidings（消息）	savings（儲金）
earnings（收入）	feelings（感情）	winnings（獎金）
belongings（財產）	greetings（問候）	

V. 動名詞的時式

1. **簡單式**：依其在句中上下文的意思及前後關係，可判斷出它的動作是與主要動詞同時發生的，或發生在主要動詞前面或後面。

　(1) **與主要動詞同時發生的**

　　　She ***is*** proud of ***being*** beautiful.（她以美麗為榮。）
　　　= She ***is*** proud that she ***is*** beautiful.

　　　He ***is*** not aware of your ***being*** so lazy.〔他（現在）不知道你（現在）這麼懶惰。〕
　　　= He ***is*** not aware that you ***are*** so lazy.

　　　I ***was*** not aware of your ***being*** so lazy.〔我（當時）不知道你（當時）是那麼懶惰。〕
　　　= I ***was*** not aware that you ***were*** so lazy.

　(2) **發生在主要動詞之前**

　　　I ***am*** proud of my son's ***dying*** in the war.（我以我兒子戰死沙場為榮。）
　　　= I ***am*** proud that my son ***died*** in the war.

　　　He ***was*** scolded for ***telling*** a lie.（他因說謊而挨罵。）
　　　= He ***was*** scolded because he ***had told*** a lie.

⑶ **發生在主要動詞之後**

> I *am* confident of our *winning*. (我相信我們會獲勝。)
> = I *am* confident that we *shall win*.

> There *is* no hope of his *succeeding*. (他沒有成功的希望。)
> = There *is* no hope that he *will succeed*.

2. **完成式**：完成式的動名詞表示**比主要動詞先發生**的動作或狀態。

> He *was* not aware of *having done* wrong. (他不知道他已經做錯了。)
> = He *was* not aware that he *had done* wrong.

> *Are* you not ashamed of (your) *having failed*? (你對你的失敗不覺得可恥嗎？)
> = *Are* you not ashamed that you *have failed*?

> He confessed *having committed* murder. (他承認他犯了謀殺罪。)
> = He *confessed* that he *had committed* murder.

> He repents of *having said* so. (他後悔曾這麼說。)
> = He *repents* that he *said* so.

【注意】 在理論上，動名詞所表示的動作時間在主要動詞之前時，該用完成式，但事實上，當上下文意已經明顯地顯示出動名詞和主要動詞的時間的前後時，通常以簡單式的動名詞代替完成式的動名詞。

> He was accused of *stealing* (= *having stolen*) a watch. (他被控偷錶。)
> = He was accused, for people believed he *had stolen* a watch.

> He was praised for *saving* (= *having saved*) a boy's life.
> (他因為救了一個男孩的命而受到讚揚。)
> = He was praised, for he *had saved* a boy's life.

> I remember *giving* (= *having given*) you my address.
> (我記得我把我的地址給你了。)
> = I remember I *have given* you my address.

VI. 動名詞的語態：被動語態動名詞表示被動之意。

What is the use of only *being praised*? (僅僅被稱讚有什麼用？)

My father doesn't like *being asked* to make a speech. (我父親不喜歡被人家邀請去演講。)

I don't mind *having been written* like this. (我不介意被寫成這樣。)

He resents *being called* a fool. (他憎恨被稱為傻瓜。)

【注意】

> **want** (需要)，**need** (需要)，**require** (需要)，**deserve** (應得)，**merit** (應得)，**bear** (適於；經得起)，**be past** (無法；不能)，**be worth** (值得) 之後如作括弧內中文解時，後接主動形式的動名詞，表示被動的意思。

> His car *wants repairing* (= to be repaired) . (他的汽車需要修理。)
>
> The wall *needs mending* (= to be mended) . (這面牆需要修補。)
>
> The trees *require trimming* (= to be trimmed) . (這些樹需要修剪。)
>
> He *deserves hanging* (= to be hanged) . (他罪該萬死。)
>
> You certainly *merit praising* (= to be praised) . (你的確應該受誇獎。)
>
> Your joke *bears repeating*. (你的笑話百聽不厭。)
> = Your joke is fit to be repeated.

The car *is past repairing*.（這輛車無法修理了。）

This book *is worth reading*.（這本書值得看。）
= This book is worthy to be read.
= This book is worthy of being read.

【註】deserve 後不可接 punishing，因為凡是動詞本身已有純粹的名詞形時，不可使用動名詞來代替純粹的名詞。

He deserved *punishing*.【誤】【有些文法書誤以為此句為正確】

He deserved *punishment*.【正】

= He deserved to be punished.（他應受處罰。）

VII. 動名詞與現在分詞的比較

1. 動名詞和現在分詞形態上相同，但**帶有名詞性質的是動名詞；帶有形容詞性質的是現在分詞**。

The *working* man dislikes *working* in the rain.（工人不喜歡在雨中工作。）
　　現在分詞　　　　　　　　動名詞

2. 動名詞和名詞一樣，可修飾名詞表該名詞的「**功用**」，現在分詞修飾名詞表該名詞的「**狀態**」，所以此時動名詞相當於名詞，現在分詞相當於形容詞。

動名詞（主重音在動名詞上）	現在分詞（主重音在名詞上）
a sléeping car（臥車）	a sleeping chíld（一個睡著了的孩子）
= a car for sleeping	= a child that is sleeping
a dáncing teacher（舞蹈老師）	a dancing béar（在跳舞的熊）
= a teacher of dancing	= a bear which dances
drínking water（飲用水）	a drinking hórse（在喝水的馬）
= water for drinking	= a horse that is drinking
a rúnning track（跑道）	running wáter（在流動的水）
= a track for running	= water that is running

VIII. 動名詞與不定詞的比較

1. 動名詞和不定詞都可表示普遍的、一般的真理、見解或信念等。

To obey / *Obeying* the law is everyone's duty.（守法是人人的義務。）

To get up / *Getting up* early is good for the health.（早起對健康有益。）

2. 除了上述一般情況外，不定詞表示尚未發生的動作；動名詞暗示已有的經驗。

You want to see him, don't you? But I think *to see*【正】/ *seeing*【誤】 him is to surrender.

（你想要見他，不是嗎？但是我認為去見他就是向他投降。）

My grandfather is a millionaire, but *having*【正】/ *to have*【誤】 money does not solve all his

problems.（我的祖父是個百萬富翁，但有錢並沒有解決他所有的問題。）

【前面已說明我祖父有錢，所以只能用動名詞，表示錢已經有了】

3. 動名詞有名詞性質，表一般的經驗；不定詞為動詞性質，表具體的、特定的事例、意見或理論。

- Would you like *seeing* the movies?（你喜歡看電影嗎？）【一般的經驗】
- Would you like *to see* the movies?（你要看電影嗎？）【特定的事例】

- On the whole, I prefer *walking* to *driving*.【一般的經驗】
  （大體上說來，我比較喜歡走路，比較不喜歡開車。）
- I prefer *to stay* at home tonight, because I'm out of sorts.【特定的意見】
  （今晚我寧願留在家裡，因為我身體不太舒服。）

4. 動名詞暗示「習慣性」。

Eating between meals is bad for the figure.（正餐之間進食對身材有害。）
→ 也可用 To eat，但是用 Eating 有強調習慣性的 "eat" 之作用。

5. 簡短的禁令用動名詞。

No *smoking*.（禁止吸煙。）　　　　　No *parking*.（禁止停車。）
No *spitting*.（禁止吐痰。）　　　　　No *loitering*.（禁止閒逛。）

6. 不定詞和動名詞都有對稱性。

To see is { *to believe*.【正】 / *believing*.【誤】 } （百聞不如一見。）

= Seeing is { *believing*.【正】 / *to believe*.【誤】 }

但不定詞和動名詞同屬一個字時，為讀音方便可以不對稱。

To understand one thing well is better than *understanding* many things by halves.
（一件事懂得很徹底，比許多事都一知半解要好。）
【如果 than 之後的 to understand 不改為 understanding，則本句就有兩個 to understand，唸起來不好聽】

To give gold to you is *giving* fuel to fire.（把金子給你等於是火上加油。）

7. 動名詞可做介詞的受詞，而不定詞不可做介詞的受詞。（除 p.411 的例外）

He is interested in { *to play*【誤】 / *playing*【正】 } hide-and-seek.（他對玩捉迷藏很有興趣。）

She is very fond of { *to dance*.【誤】 / *dancing*.【正】 } （她非常喜歡跳舞。）

8. 在 *way*, *pleasure*, *time*, *chance*, *opportunity*, *plan*, *power* 等名詞之後可接 *of* + 動名詞或不定詞（to + 原形動詞）。

Do you know the *way* { *of mastering* / *to master* } English?（你知道精通英語之道嗎？）

I had no *chance* { *of speaking* / *to speak* } to him.（我沒有機會和他說話。）

I am glad to have an *opportunity* { *of seeing* / *to see* } you.（我很高興有機會見到你。）

【註 1】在 *ability*, *tendency*, *resolution*, *determination*, *ambition*, *attempt*, *desire*, *effort*, *failure*, *refusal*, *promise* 等字之後，不可接 **of** + ～**ing**，可接不定詞的形式。

He has no **ability** { *of translating*【誤】 / **to translate**【正】 } the novel.

（他沒有能力翻譯這本小說。）

He burns with an **ambition** { *of winning*【誤】 / **to win**【正】 } fame.（他熱衷於成名。）

Please make an **effort** { *of arriving*【誤】 / **to arrive**【正】 } early.（請儘量早點到。）

His **failure** { *of attaining*【誤】 / **to attain**【正】 } his goal made him quite disappointed.

（他不能達到目標使他很失望。）

上述名詞中有些可接 *of* 以外的其他介詞。

He has an **ability in** *writing*.【ability 之後可接 in】
（他有寫作的能力。）

His **desire for** *a promotion* is pathetic.【desire 之後可接 for】
（他對升遷的渴望怪可憐的。）

He showed great **resolution in** *carrying out the plan*.【resolution 之後可接 in】
（在執行這計劃時，他展現了極大的決心。）

His **efforts at** *clearing up the mystery* failed.【effort 之後可接 at】
（他企圖解開這個謎所做的努力失敗了。）

【註 2】在 *idea*, *habit*, *method*, *purpose* 等字之後通常接 **of** + ～**ing**，不可接不定詞。

They got the happy idea { *to climb*【誤】 / **of climbing**【正】 } the hill.

（他們想到爬山的好主意。）

I am in the habit { *to rise early.*【誤】 / **of rising early.**【正】 }（我習慣早起。）

He has introduced a new method { *to teach*【誤】 / **of teaching**【正】 } a foreign language.

（他介紹了一種新的外語教學法。）

He went abroad for the purpose { *to study*【誤】 / **of studying**【正】 } music.

（他出國是為了學音樂。）

9. 下面片語之後可接動名詞和不定詞，但所表示的意義不同。

> *on one's way to + V*　表示在走路過程中。
> *on one's way to + ～ing*　表示在「成為某種地位」的過程中。

She was *on her way to catch* the school bus.（她在趕搭校車的途中。）

He is *on his way to becoming* a journalist.（他將會成為一個新聞記者。）

10. **動名詞和不定詞都可作爲動詞的受詞**

⑴ 下列動詞（片語）可接動名詞或不定詞爲其受詞，意義上無太大的差別。

①　begin（開始），continue（繼續），commence（開始），discontinue（停止）

It began $\left\{\begin{array}{l}\textit{to rain.}\\\textit{raining.}\end{array}\right.$（開始下雨了。）

The traffic continued $\left\{\begin{array}{l}\textit{to move}\\\textit{moving}\end{array}\right\}$ slowly.（車流依然移動得很慢。）

She started $\left\{\begin{array}{l}\textit{to write}\\\textit{writing}\end{array}\right\}$ a letter.（她開始寫信。）

【註】若是表示「**認識**」或「**了解**」時，該用不定詞，因爲動名詞有連續進行的意味，認識與了解卻只是短暫間的事情。

I began $\left\{\begin{array}{l}\textit{to understand}【正】\\\textit{understanding}【誤】\end{array}\right\}$ him.（我開始了解他。）

She started $\left\{\begin{array}{l}\textit{to realize}【正】\\\textit{realizing}【誤】\end{array}\right\}$ the situation.（她開始了解這個情況。）

②　attempt（試圖），intend（打算），plan（計劃）

Don't attempt $\left\{\begin{array}{l}\textit{to do}\\\textit{doing}\end{array}\right\}$ it by yourself.（不要想自己做它。）

I intend $\left\{\begin{array}{l}\textit{to go}\\\textit{going}\end{array}\right\}$ abroad shortly.（我打算不久就出國。）

I plan $\left\{\begin{array}{l}\textit{to take}\\\textit{on taking}\end{array}\right\}$ German next year.（我計劃明年選修德文。）

③　decline（拒絕），dislike（不喜歡），dread（害怕），detest（憎惡），fear（害怕），hate（討厭），like（喜歡），love（愛），neglect（忽略），omit（省略），prefer（比較喜歡），can't bear (stand, endure)（不能忍受）

We dislike $\left\{\begin{array}{l}\textit{to play}\\\textit{playing}\end{array}\right\}$ bridge.（我們不喜歡玩橋牌。）

I dread $\left\{\begin{array}{l}\textit{to think}\\\textit{thinking}\end{array}\right\}$ about it.（我怕去想它。）

Everyone hates $\left\{\begin{array}{l}\textit{to wait}\\\textit{waiting}\end{array}\right\}$ for buses.（每個人都討厭等公車。）

He neglected $\left\{\begin{array}{l}\textit{to file}\\\textit{filing}\end{array}\right\}$ his income tax return.（他忽略了把他所得稅的申報書歸檔。）

I can't stand $\left\{\begin{array}{l}\textit{to see}\\\textit{seeing}\end{array}\right\}$ her cry.（我受不了看她哭。）

【註 1】 like, love, hate 接不定詞常表示主詞本身的愛惡；接動名詞時可表示主詞本身及主詞對別人的愛惡。

    I *like to swim*. (我喜歡游泳。——主詞本身的喜愛)

    I *like swimming*. 〔我喜歡游泳。(或) 我喜歡看別人游泳。〕

【註 2】 「should (would) like + 不定詞」等於 want。

    I *would like to have* a single room with a bath. (我想要有浴室的單人房。)

    I *should like to take* a walk in the morning. (我想要早上散步。)

【註 3】 like 作 "think it wise *or* right" 解時，接不定詞；作 "enjoy" 解時接動名詞。

    I *like to go* to the dentist twice a year.

    (我認為一年看兩次牙醫是明智的。)【like = think it wise】

    She *likes playing* with her sister. (她喜歡和她的妹妹玩。)【likes = enjoys】

【註 4】 prefer + 動名詞…(to + 動名詞)(參照 p.204)
         = prefer to + 原形動詞…(rather than + 原形動詞)

    She *prefers dancing to singing*. (她喜歡跳舞，不喜歡唱歌。)

    = She *prefers to dance rather than sing*.

    I *prefer staying in to going out*. (我喜歡留在室內，不喜歡出去。)

    = I *prefer to stay in rather than go out*.

⑵ **下列動詞可接動名詞或不定詞為受詞，但意義上有出入。**

① remember, forget, regret +
    不定詞 —— 動作尚未發生
    動名詞 —— 動作已經發生

    I will *remember to mail* the letter. (我會記得寄信。)
    I *remember mailing* the letter. (我記得曾把信寄出。)

    I'm afraid he will *forget to write* to me. (我擔心他會忘記寫信給我。)
    I shall never *forget seeing* the Alps for the first time.
    (我永遠忘不了第一次看到阿爾卑斯山的情形。)

    I *regret to say* that we don't have it in stock. (很抱歉，那樣東西我們沒有存貨。)
    So you *regret having said* such a thing. (所以你後悔說了這樣一件事。)

② try, propose, mean + 不定詞時表示「意欲；打算」，接動名詞則各有不同意義

    Try to get here early. (儘量早點來這裡。) —— 儘量，企圖，試著
    I *tried cooking* meat in wine instead of water.
    (我嘗試用酒煮肉而不用水煮。) —— 試驗

    She *proposes to start* tomorrow. (她想明天出發。) —— 意欲
    I *propose waiting* till he comes. (我建議等到他來。) —— 建議

    I don't *mean to cheat* him. (我不想騙他。) —— 意欲
    Here is the blow of the trumpet. It *means attack*.
    (號角聲響了，這意味著攻擊。) —— 意味

③ stop + { 不定詞 —— 停下來，開始去做某事
           { 動名詞 —— 停止做某事

{ I *stopped to eat.* = I stopped in order to eat.（我停下來吃東西。）
{ I *stopped eating.*（我停止吃東西。）

④ go on + { 不定詞 —— 有間斷的繼續
            { 動名詞 —— 無間斷的繼續

Having read Lesson 4, she *goes on to read* Lesson 5.
（讀完了第四課之後，她接著讀第五課。）
She *goes on reading* Lesson 5.（她繼續讀第五課。）

⑤ learn + { 不定詞 —— 學會了
            { 動名詞 —— 學習，和 study 同義

Although he is only six, he has *learned to skate* skillfully.
（他雖然才六歲，但是他已經學會溜冰。）
He has been *learning skating* for three years and he still falls down all the time.
（他學溜冰三年了，依然總是會摔倒。）

⑥ be afraid of + 動名詞 —— 只表害怕
   be afraid + 不定詞 —— 表因害怕而不敢去做

He *is afraid of falling.*（他怕會掉下來。）
He *was afraid to swim* so he stayed at home.（他害怕去游泳，所以他留在家裡。）

(3) **下列動詞及片語之後只可接動名詞為受詞，不可接不定詞。**

abominate（憎恨）　acknowledge（承認）　avoid（避免）　admit（承認）
anticipate（期待）　appreciate（感激）　break off（突然停止）　burst out（突然）
complete（完成）　confess（招認）　consider（認為）　contemplate（打算）
defend（保護）　defer（延緩）　delay（延遲）　deny（否認）　enjoy（喜歡）
escape（逃避）　evade（逃避）　excuse（原諒）　envy（羨慕）　fancy（想像）
finish（完成）　forgive（原諒）　have done（完成）　hinder（妨礙）　imagine（想像）
involve（牽涉）　loathe（厭惡）　leave off（中止）　mind（介意）　miss（錯過）
postpone（延遲）　pardon（寬恕）　practice（練習）　put off（延期）　quit（停止）
recall（回想）　resent（憎恨）　repent（後悔）　recollect（回想）　report（報告）
resist（抵抗）　risk（冒險）　suggest（建議）　tolerate（忍受）　understand（了解）
can't help (avoid, prevent)（不得不；忍不住）

He *admitted taking* the key.（他承認拿了鑰匙。）
We would *appreciate hearing* from you.（我們會感謝你的來信。）
He *avoided meeting* me.（他避免和我見面。）
He *escaped being hurt* in the accident.（他逃過了在車禍中受傷。）
He *considered going* to college.（他考慮上大學。）
I have just *finished typing* my paper.（我剛打完我的文件。）

I *enjoyed **talking*** with him.（我喜歡和他談話。）

I'm sorry that I *missed **seeing*** you.（我很抱歉錯過和你碰面的機會。）

I can't *fancy* his ***doing*** such a thing.（我不能想像他會做這種事。）

*Imagine **winning*** the Irish sweepstakes!（如果能中愛爾蘭賽馬的特獎該有多好！）

She *resented **being*** called a baby.（她討厭人家叫她小孩。）

I was unable to *resist **laughing***.（我忍不住想笑。）

He has *quit **drinking***.（他已戒酒。）

⑷ **下列動詞之後用不定詞當受詞：**

① **下列動詞只可接不定詞，不可接動名詞做受詞**

agree（同意）　afford（負擔得起）　arrange（安排）　consent（同意） care（想要）　contrive（設法）　decide（決定）　determine（決定） endeavour（努力）　fail（未能）　guarantee（保證）　hesitate（猶豫） hope（希望）　hurry（趕快）　manage（設法）　offer（提議）　pretend（假裝） promise（答應）　seek（試圖）　prepare（準備）　refuse（拒絕）　resolve（決心） swear（發誓）　think（打算）　undertake（保證；約定）

I don't *care **to see*** him again.（我不想再見到他。）

We have *decided* not ***to go***.（我們已決定不去了。）

The club *endeavored **to raise*** $5,000 for charity.（該俱樂部努力籌募五千元給慈善機構。）

We *hope **to see*** you soon.（我們希望能很快就見到你。）

He *pretended **to be*** ill.（他假裝生病。）

He *refuses **to eat***.（他拒絕進食。）

He *swore **to speak*** the truth.（他發誓要說實話。）

He has *promised **to get*** me a position.（他答應給我安插一個職位。）

= He has promised me a position.

I will *guarantee **to prove*** every statement I made.（我保證會證實我所做的每項聲明。）

He *undertook **to raise*** the funds.（他保證要籌募資金。）

He *undertook **to be*** here at ten o'clock.（他答應十點到這裡來。）

② **下列動詞須先接名詞或代名詞做受詞，再接不定詞做受詞補語**

ask（要求）　allow（允許）　advise（勸告）　cause（使）　command（命令） compel（強迫）　enable（使能夠）　encourage（鼓勵）　forbid（禁止） force（強迫）　get（使）　instruct（教導）　invite（邀請）　oblige（強制） order（命令）　permit（允許）　persuade（說服）　press（壓迫）　remind（提醒） request（請求）　recommend（勸告；建議）　teach（教）　tell（告訴） tempt（誘惑）　urge（催促）　warn（警告）

I *allow* him ***to smoke***.（我允許他抽煙。）

I *advise* you ***to be*** honest.（我勸你要誠實。）

She *compelled* me ***to sleep***.（她強迫我睡覺。）

His kindness *causes* people ***to like*** him.（他的仁慈使得人們喜歡他。）

Mary *encouraged* me ***to go*** swimming.（瑪麗鼓勵我去游泳。）

The committee *forced* him *to resign*.（委員會強迫他辭職。）

He *ordered* us not *to speak* so loudly.（他命令我們不准這麼大聲說話。）

He *urged* me *to study* French.（他催促我學法文。）

They *warned* me not *to go* this way.（他們警告我不要走這條路。）

【註 1】advise, allow, permit, recommend 等字後接「人」為受詞時用不定詞；若是沒有接「人」時則用動名詞。

比較 {
I don't *allow* (*permit*) him *to swim*.（我不允許他游泳。）
I don't *allow* (*permit*) *swimming* here.（我不許在此地游泳。）
}

{
I *recommend* (*advise*) you *to take* vitamin pills.（我建議你吃維他命丸。）
I *recommend* (*advise*) *taking* vitamin pills.（我建議吃維他命丸。）
}

{
Circumstances do not *permit* me *to help* you.（環境不許可我幫助你。）
Circumstances do not *permit* **my helping** you.
【動名詞 helping 當然也可有其意義上的主詞 my】
}

【註 2】refuse, hope, suggest, insist, demand, appreciate 等字接受詞再接不定詞的觀念是錯誤的。

He *refused me to use* his car.【誤】

He refused to let me use his car.【正】（他拒絕我使用他的車子。）

I *hope you to have* a good time.【誤】

I hope you will have a good time.【正】（我希望你玩得愉快。）

③ **下列動詞可直接接不定詞做受詞，或先接名詞（代名詞），再接不定詞**

ask（要求）　beg（懇求）　choose（選擇）　dare（敢）　desire（想）　expect（期待）
hate（憎恨）　help（幫忙）　intend（打算）　like（喜歡）　love（愛）　mean（意欲）
prefer（比較喜歡）　promise（答應）　trouble（麻煩）　want（想要）　wish（但願）

{
They *asked to come* in.（他們要求要進來。）
They *asked us to come* in.（他們要求我們進來。）
}

{
The boy *begged to go*.（這男孩請求要去。）
The boy *begged me to go*.（這男孩請求我去。）
}

{
I *expect to meet* him.（我預期會見到他。）
I *expect you to meet* him.（我想要你見他。）
}

{
She *helped* (*to*) *push* the car.（她幫忙推車子。）
She *helped him* (*to*) *push* the car.（她幫他推車子。）
}

④ **下列動詞只可用 "to be" 和 "to have" 二個不定詞做受詞補語，或是用名詞子句當受詞補語**

acknowledge（承認）　believe（相信）　calculate（計算）　consider（認為）
declare（宣布）　estimate（估計）　feel（感覺）　find（發現）　guess（猜想）
imagine（想像）　know（知道）　maintain（堅稱）　reckon（認為）　see（了解）
suppose（猜想）　take（以為）　understand（了解）

{
I *consider* him (*to be*) the best candidate.（我認為他是最好的候選人。）
= I *consider* that he *is* the best candidate.
}

$\begin{cases} \text{I } \textit{estimate} \text{ it } \textbf{\textit{to be}} \text{ about five pounds in weight.} （我估計它大約五磅重。） \\ = \text{I } \textit{estimate} \text{ that it } \textit{is} \text{ about five pounds in weight.} \end{cases}$

$\begin{cases} \text{I } \textit{know} \text{ him } \textbf{\textit{to be}} \text{ dependable.} （我知道他是可靠的。） \\ = \text{I } \textit{know} \text{ that he } \textit{is} \text{ dependable.} \end{cases}$

$\begin{cases} \text{They } \textit{considered} \text{ him } \textbf{\textit{to have}} \text{ more ability than the others.} \\ = \text{They } \textit{considered} \text{ that he } \textit{had} \text{ more ability than the others.} \\ （他們認爲他比其他的人有能力。） \end{cases}$

⑤ **下列動詞常接 how 再接不定詞**

> discover（發現）　explain（解釋）　find out（查出）　wonder（想知道）

I *discovered* **how to solve** the problem.（我發現如何解決此問題。）

He *explained* **how to use** the parachute.（他解釋如何使用降落傘。）

She *found out* **how to work** quickly.（她查出如何快速工作的方法。）

They *wonder* **how to finish** the job.（他們想知道如何完成這個工作。）

IX. 動名詞的慣用語

1. ***There is no* + ~*ing*** = It is impossible to + V（…是不可能的）
   = No one can + V
   = We cannot + V

   There is no telling what may happen.（誰也不知道將會發生什麼事。）
   = *It is impossible to tell* what may happen.
   = *No one can tell* what may happen.
   There was no going out that night because of the typhoon.
   = *It was impossible to go out* that night because of the typhoon.
   = *We could not go out* that night because of the typhoon.
   （那天晚上因爲有颱風，我們無法出去。）

2. *feel like* + ~*ing* = be inclined to + V（想要…）
   I don't ***feel like studying*** tonight.（今晚我不想讀書。）
   I don't ***feel like eating*** (*drinking*, *sleeping*, etc.) just now.〔我此刻不想吃（喝、睡等）。〕

   feel like + N，有不同意思，比較下面兩個句子：

   It ***feels like*** wood (glass, silk, etc.).〔那摸起來像木頭（玻璃、絲等）。〕
   I don't ***feel like*** a walk just now.（現在我不想去散步。）

3. *on* (*or upon*) + ~*ing* = as soon as（一…就）
   On hearing the news, she turned pale.（一聽到這消息，她臉色發白。）
   = *As soon as she heard* the news, she turned pale.

4. *No* + ~*ing* = Let there be no + ~*ing*（不准…）
   = You must not + V

   No smoking.（不准吸煙。）
   = *Let there be no smoking.* = *You must not smoke.*
   No talking in class.（上課時不准談話。）
   = *Let there be no talking* in class. = *You must not talk* in class.

5. **of one's own** + ~ing（自己…的）

This picture is **of his own painting**.（這幅畫是他自己畫的。）

His house was **of his own planning**.（他的房子是他自己規劃的。）

It is a profession **of his own choosing**.（那是他自己選擇的職業。）

6. **It goes without saying that**… = It is needless to say that…（…是不用說的）

It goes without saying that diligence is the key to success.

= *It is needless to say* that diligence is the key to success.

（勤勉是成功的秘訣這是不用說的。）

7. **be on** (*or* **upon, at**) **the point of** + ~ing = **be on the verge of** + ~ing

= **be about to** + V（原形）（快要…）

On being sent to the hospital, he **was on the point of breathing** his last.

= When he was sent to the hospital, he *was about to breathe* his last.

（他被送到醫院的時候已經快死了。）

The baby was **on the point of crying** when her mother finally came home.

= The baby's mother came home just as the baby *was about to cry*.

（正當小孩快要哭的時候，她的母親終於回來了。）

The coach was **at the point of giving up** the game when our team scored two points.

= Just as the coach *was about to give up* the game, we scored two points.

（正當教練準備放棄比賽時，我們這一隊竟得了兩分。）

8. **make a point of** + ~ing = make it a point to + V（認為～是必要的；很重視～）

He **makes a point of remembering** each one of our birthdays.

= He *makes it a point to remember* each one of our birthdays.

（他認為記住我們每個人的生日是必要的。）

I always **make a point of getting up** early.（我總是很注重早起。）

= I always *make it a point to get up* early.

9. **never** (*or* **not**) …**without** + ~ing = whenever…, …（沒有…而不～；每…必～）

He **never** comes **without** bringing some present.

= *Whenever* he comes, he brings some present.

（他從來沒有不帶禮物就來了。── 他每次來都有帶禮物。）

He does **not** go (*or* **never** goes) out **without** losing his umbrella.（他每次出去都會把傘弄丟。）

= *Whenever* he goes out, he loses his umbrella.

I **never** see her **without** thinking of her mother.（我每次見到她，都想起她母親。）

= *Whenever* I see her, I think of her mother.

10. **What do you say to** + ~ing?（參照 p.148）

= What do you think of + ~ing?

The cherry blossoms on Mt. Grass are now at their best. **What do you say to going** there if it is fine tomorrow?

〔草山（陽明山）的櫻花現在正盛開。如果明天天氣好，我們去那裡玩好不好？〕

* 此結構後面也可直接接名詞

What do you say to a short walk?（出去散一下步，你覺得如何？）

11. ***How about* + ～*ing*?**（參照 p.148）

= What (do you think) about + ～ing?

How about going for a walk after dinner?（晚飯後去散散步如何？）

How about going to France for our holidays?（我們去法國渡假如何？）

12. ***It is no use*** (*or **no good***) + ～*ing*（…是沒有用的）

= ***There is no use*** (*in*) + ～*ing*

= ***It is of no use*** $\begin{cases} \textbf{\textit{to}} + \textbf{\textit{V}}（原形） \\ + \sim\textbf{\textit{ing}}【參照世界書局四用辭典 p.1821】 \end{cases}$ = It is useless to + V（原形）

It is no use crying.（哭是沒有用的。）

= ***There is no use*** (*in*) ***crying.***

= ***It is of no use*** $\begin{cases} \textbf{\textit{to cry.}} \\ \textbf{\textit{crying.}} \end{cases}$

= *It is useless to cry.*

It is no use (*or **good***) ***making*** an excuse for this.〔找藉口（編造個理由）是沒有用的。〕

It is no use trying to deceive me.（想騙我是沒有用的。）

It wasn't much use *your **pretending*** to be sick.（你假裝生病是沒多大用處的。）

【註】在口語中可用 It is no use to + V（原形），如：It is no use to talk.（談也沒有用。）

13. $\left.\begin{array}{l} \textbf{\textit{cannot help}} \\ = \textbf{\textit{cannot avoid}} \\ = \textbf{\textit{cannot forbear}} \\ = \textbf{\textit{cannot resist}} \\ = \textbf{\textit{cannot}} \left\{\begin{array}{l}\textbf{\textit{keep}}\\\textbf{\textit{refrain}}\\\textbf{\textit{abstain}}\\\textbf{\textit{desist}}\end{array}\right\} \textbf{\textit{from}} \\ = \textbf{\textit{cannot}} \left\{\begin{array}{l}\textbf{\textit{hold}}\\\textbf{\textit{keep}}\end{array}\right\} \textbf{\textit{back from}} \end{array}\right\}$ + ～*ing*（不得不…；忍不住…）

= cannot (choose) but + V（原形）

$\begin{cases} \textbf{I}\ \textbf{\textit{could not help smiling}}\ \text{at the idea.}（對於這個想法，我忍不住想笑。）\\ = \text{I}\ \textit{could not avoid smiling}\ \text{at the idea.}\\ = \text{I}\ \textit{could not forbear smiling}\ \text{at the idea.}\\ = \text{I}\ \textit{could not resist smiling}\ \text{at the idea.} \end{cases}$

$\begin{cases} = \text{I}\ \textit{could not keep from smiling}\ \text{at the idea.}\\ = \text{I}\ \textit{could not refrain from smiling}\ \text{at the idea.}\\ = \text{I}\ \textit{could not abstain from smiling}\ \text{at the idea.}\\ = \text{I}\ \textit{could not desist from smiling}\ \text{at the idea.} \end{cases}$

$\begin{cases} = \text{I}\ \textit{could not hold back from smiling}\ \text{at the idea.}\\ = \text{I}\ \textit{could not keep back from smiling}\ \text{at the idea.} \end{cases}$

= I *could not* (*choose*) *but smile* at the idea.

14. *do a lot of* (*or much*) + *~ing* = *~* a lot of (*or* much) (…做得很多)

They *did too much drinking* last night. (昨天晚上他們喝太多酒。)
= They *drank too much* last night.

Do you *do much fishing*? (你常常釣魚嗎？)
= Do you *fish much*?

When I get to Rome, I want to *do a lot of sightseeing*.
= When I get to Rome, I want to *see a lot of sights*.
(我到羅馬時，我要遊覽很多名勝古蹟。)

【類例】 She still *does a little singing*. (她仍然偶爾會唱歌。)
= She still *sings a little*.

15. *go* + *~ing* = *go a-~ing* (*~*ing 大部分指運動或遊戲)

He *went fishing* with his uncle. (他跟他叔叔去釣魚。)
= He *went a-fishing* with his uncle.

Mrs. Jones *went shopping* last night. (瓊斯太太昨晚去購物。)
= Mrs. Jones *went a-shopping* last night.

【注意】 **a-fishing** 的 **a-** 為介詞 **on** 的縮寫，而 go on 的意思是「去做~」。go a-fishing 是古代英文的形式，而今多用 go fishing 的形式。**go 後面的 ~ing 究竟是動名詞還是現在分詞，文法專家們意見不一致**，有些人認為 ~ing 是動名詞，做介詞 on 的受詞，後來介詞 on 省略了；另一些人則認為 go 後面的 ~ing 和 come, sit, stand, lie 後的 ~ing 用法應該相同，此時 go 後的 ~ing 已完全由動名詞轉變為現在分詞，做主詞補語。

比較下面用法：

go {
bathing (去洗澡)
bowling (去打保齡球)
boating (去划船)
camping (去露營)
fishing (去釣魚)
golfing (去打高爾夫球)
hunting (去打獵)
mountain climbing (去爬山)
picnicking (去野餐)
riding (去騎馬)
rowing (去划船)
skating (去溜冰)
skiing (去滑雪)
shooting (去射擊)
shopping (去購物)
swimming (去游泳)
vacationing (去渡假)
⋮
}

come {
crying (哭著來)
hurrying (趕著來)
running (跑著來)
shouting (喊著來)
singing (唱著來)
⋮
}

sit (stand, lie) {
gazing〔坐（站，躺）著注視〕
listening to〔坐（站，躺）著聽〕
reading〔坐（站，躺）著讀〕
talking〔坐（站，躺）著談〕
thinking〔坐（站，躺）著想〕
watching〔坐（站，躺）著看〕
⋮
}

16. *worth* + ~*ing*（值得…）

(1) **worth 當形容詞用時帶有介詞性質**（參照 p.194）後面可接名詞或動名詞爲其受詞，接動名詞時有三個條件必須遵守，即**主動的，及物動詞，但無受詞。**

The place is well *worth a visit* in the evening.（這個地方非常值得在晚上來。）

The museum is *worth* { *being seen.*【誤】 / *seeing.*【正】 }（這博物館值得一看。）

His advice is *worth* { *being taken.*【誤】 / *taking.*【正】 }（他的忠告值得採納。）

Is this plan *worth* { *trying it*【誤】 / *trying*【正】 } once more at such a great expense?

（這項計劃值不值得花如此龐大的費用再度嘗試？）

This question is *worth* { *discussing it*【誤】 / *discussing*【正】 } further.（這個問題值得更進一步地討論。）

(2) 有關 worth 的句型

> 主詞（含 it）+ be worth + ~ing
> It（虛主詞）+ be worth while（或 worthwhile）+ 不定詞或動名詞（眞主詞）

It（= This book）is *worth reading* carefully.〔它（這本書）值得精讀。〕

It is *worthwhile* to read (*or* reading) this book carefully.

【註 1】 **worthy** 之後，和其他形容詞一樣可接介詞 +（動）名詞，也可接不定詞，但主動、被動要分清楚。

He is *worthy* { of filling / to fill } the post.（他能夠擔任此一職務。）

He is no more *worthy* { of being called / to be called } your son.（他不配再被稱爲你的兒子。）

This is *worthy* of remembrance.（這是值得紀念的。）
= This is *worthy* of being remembered.
= This is *worthy* to be remembered.

【註 2】 worthy 可放在名詞前，修飾該名詞。

He has lived a *worthy* life.（他過著有價值的生活。）

【註 3】 while 是名詞，前面可加所有格（my, your…），在現代英語中，**worth while** 常連成一個字，即 **worthwhile**。

It is *worth my while* to do this.（我做這件事是值得的。）
= It is *worthwhile for me* to do this.

17. *above* + *~ing*（不屑；不願）（參照 p.664）

    If you want to learn, you must not be *above asking* questions.

    （如果你想要學習，便必須不恥下問。）

    He is *above telling* a lie.（他不屑於說謊。）

18. *have*
$\begin{cases} \textit{difficulty} \\ \textit{trouble} \\ \textit{fun} \\ \textit{a hard time} \\ \textit{a good time} \end{cases}$
(in) + *~ing*

have 當「有」解釋，後接情感名詞時，後面的 **in** 常省略，再加動名詞的形式。

We *had great difficulty* (*in*) *solving* the problem.

（我們對解決這問題有很大的困難。）

I *have trouble* (*in*) *getting* the car started.

（我要發動這汽車有困難。）

I *have fun* (*in*) *speaking* English.（我覺得說英文很有趣。）

Poor Susan *had a hard time* (*in*) *trying* to get the children to go to bed.

（可憐的蘇珊，不容易打發孩子們就寢。）

We *had a good time* (*in*) *playing* tennis.（我們打網球打得很愉快。）

  【註 1】*take the trouble to* 須接動詞原形。

        You needn't have *taken the trouble to* do it for me.

        （你不必費心為我做那件事。）

  【註 2】*have a hard time* 後面接否定動作時，須接不定詞。

        He was so funny that I had a hard time *not to burst out laughing*.

        （他是如此的有趣，以致於我很難忍住不笑出來。）

19. $\begin{cases} \textit{come} \\ \textit{go} \end{cases}$ *near* (*to*) + *~ing*（幾乎要…）

= *come close to* + *~ing*

= be almost + p.p.

= nearly + V

He *came* (*or went*) *near* (*to*) *being* drowned.（他幾乎淹死。）

= He *came close to being* drowned.

= He *was almost* drowned.

The army *came near* (*to*) *obtaining* a complete victory.（這軍隊幾乎獲得全勝。）

= The army *nearly obtained* a complete victory.

20. *for the + ~ing*（只要）

= if one only + 原形動詞

You may have it *for the asking*.（你要就拿去。）
= You may have it *if you only ask*.

The choicest gold is to be had *for the digging*.
（最上等的黃金只要挖掘就可以得到。）

It is yours *for the asking*.（你要就送給你。）

21. *far from + ~ing*（絕非；一點也不）

= not at all; instead of

I am *far from* blaming him.（我一點也不怪他。）
= I do *not* blame him *at all*.

His explanation is *far from* (*being*) satisfactory.
= His explanation is *not at all* satisfactory.
（他的解釋一點也不令人滿意。）

【far from 接形容詞可視為形容詞前的 being 省略】

Far from（= *Instead of*）admiring his paintings, I dislike them intensely.
（我不但不讚美，反而非常討厭他的畫。）

22. **有些片語中的 to 是當介詞用，後面該接（動）名詞為受詞，不可接原形動詞。**

Mrs. Brown *applied herself to making* a flower garden out of her backyard.
（布朗太太集中精力要把她的後院弄成一座花園。）

We *are used to sitting* up late.（我們習慣於熬夜到很晚。）

He *devoted himself to writing* a thesis.（他致力於寫論文。）

They *fell to eating* with great vigor.
（他們開始狼吞虎嚥地吃了起來。）

I am *looking forward to seeing* you.（我期待能見到你。）

In addition to advising him, I gave him five hundred dollars.
（我除了勸告他之外，還給了他五百元。）

Nobody *objects to raising* funds for the monument.
（沒有人反對募款建紀念碑。）

He *took to going* for a walk every night before he went to bed.
（他喜歡每晚就寢之前散散步。）

【類例】下面片語中的 to 是介系詞：

according to（根據）

accustom oneself to（使習慣於）

add to（增加）

adhere to（黏著；堅持）

admit to（承認）

amount to（總計；等於）

apply oneself to（致力於）

as to（關於）

be accustomed to（習慣於）

be addicted to（沉迷於；對…上癮）

be adjusted to（調整）

be annexed to（附加）

be committed to（致力於）

be converted to（使轉變成）

be dedicated to（致力於）

be devoted to（致力於）

be equal to（等於）

be faithful to（忠於）

be familiar to（為…所熟知）

be opposed to（反對）

be reduced to（淪落到…狀態）

be sentenced to（被判…刑）

cling to（附著；堅持）

come to（談到）

commit oneself to（致力於）

confess to（招認）

defer to（順從）

dedicate oneself to（致力於）

devote oneself to（致力於）

due to（由於）

fall to（開始）

feel equal to（能勝任）

feel up to（能勝任）

get to（開始）

habituate oneself to（習慣於）

have an objection to（反對）

in addition to（除了…之外）

in (*or* with) regard to（關於）

in reference to（關於）

in relation to（關於）

in respect to（關於）

inferior to（比…差）

lower oneself to（貶低自己去…）

loyal to（忠於）

next to（幾乎）

object to（反對）

owing to（由於）

own to（承認）

reply to（回答）

resort to（訴諸）

response to（回答）

say to（叫；命）

see to（注意）

stick to（堅持）

subject to（依照；受制於）

superior to（優於）

surrender to（向…屈服）

swear to（保證）

take exception to（反對）

take to（喜歡）

with a view to（為了）

with an eye to（為了）

yield to（向…屈服）

第三章 分 詞（**Participles**）

I. **定義：** 分詞是具有形容詞性質的動詞形態，分為**現在分詞**（Present Participle）與**過去分詞**（Past Participle）兩種。

II. **形式：**

時式\語態\例		**write**（及物動詞）		**rise**（不及物動詞）	
		主　　動	被　　動	主　　動	被　動
現在分詞	簡　單	writing	being written	rising	無
	完　成	having written	having been written	having risen	無
過　去　分　詞		無	written	risen	無

III. **分詞的性質：** 分詞具有動詞性質，所以可以接補語或受詞，也可有副詞（片語）或副詞子句修飾它。含有分詞及其受詞、補語或副詞的字群為**分詞片語**。

The boy *sitting in the corner* is my nephew.（坐在角落的男孩是我的姪子。）

（副詞片語 修飾 sitting；分詞片語當形容詞用 修飾 boy）

IV. **分詞的用法：**

1. **作為主要動詞的一部分：**

⑴ be + 現在分詞 → 進行式

She was *sleeping* when I came in.（我進來的時候她正在睡覺。）

⑵ be + 不及物動詞的過去分詞 → 代替完成式

Winter was *gone*.（冬天過去了。）

⑶ be + 及物動詞的過去分詞 → 被動態

This letter was *written* by my mother.（這封信是我母親寫的。）

My purse was *stolen* yesterday.（我的錢包昨天被偷了。）

⑷ have + 過去分詞 → 完成式

He has *bought* a piece of land near Taipei.（他在台北附近買了一塊地。）

The train had *gone* when I arrived at the station.（當我到達車站時火車已經開了。）

2. **作為名詞的修飾語：**

⑴ **現在分詞和過去分詞均可修飾名詞，但意義不同：**

① **現在分詞表主動及進行的意思，作形容詞用的現在分詞，可以改成「動詞為主動的形容詞子句」。**

A *rolling* stone gathers no moss.（滾石不生苔；轉業不聚財。）

= A stone *which is rolling* gathers no moss.

The gentleman *standing* over there is our principal.

= The gentleman *who is standing* over there is our principal.

（站在那邊的那位紳士是我們的校長。）

其他的例子：

$$\begin{cases} \text{a } \textit{sleeping} \text{ baby（正在睡覺的嬰兒）} \\ = \text{a baby } \textit{who is sleeping} \end{cases}$$ $$\begin{cases} \text{a } \textit{charming} \text{ girl（迷人的女孩）} \\ = \text{a girl } \textit{who is charming} \end{cases}$$

$$\begin{cases} \text{an } \textit{interesting} \text{ story（有趣的故事）} \\ = \text{a story } \textit{which is interesting} \end{cases}$$ $$\begin{cases} \text{a } \textit{running} \text{ dog（正在跑的狗）} \\ = \text{a dog } \textit{which is running} \end{cases}$$

② **及物動詞的過去分詞表被動的意思**，作形容詞用的過去分詞，可以改為「**動詞為被動的形容詞子句**」。

Lost time is lost forever.（失去的時間永遠失去了。）

= Time *which is lost* is lost forever.

I received a letter *written* in English.（我收到一封用英文寫的信。）

= I received a letter *which was written* in English.

其他的例子：

$$\begin{cases} \text{a } \textit{broken} \text{ glass（破的杯子）} \\ = \text{a glass } \textit{which is broken} \end{cases}$$ $$\begin{cases} \text{a } \textit{wounded} \text{ soldier（受傷的士兵）} \\ = \text{a soldier } \textit{who is} \text{ (or } \textit{was) wounded} \end{cases}$$

③ **有些不及物動詞的過去分詞表主動的意思，完成的狀態**。此種作形容詞用的過去分詞，可改成「**動詞為主動的形容詞子句**」。

The ground is covered with the *fallen* leaves.（地面覆蓋著落葉。）

= The ground is covered with the leaves *which have fallen*.

She wore a *faded* coat.（她穿著一件褪了色的外套。）

= She wore a coat *whose color had faded*.

其他的例子：

$$\begin{cases} \text{a } \textit{returned} \text{ soldier（歸來的士兵）} \\ = \text{a soldier } \textit{who has returned} \end{cases}$$ $$\begin{cases} \text{a } \textit{learned} \text{ man（有學問的人）} \\ = \text{a man } \textit{who is of much learning} \end{cases}$$

$$\begin{cases} \text{a } \textit{faded} \text{ flower（凋謝的花）} \\ = \text{a flower } \textit{which has faded} \end{cases}$$ $$\begin{cases} \text{a } \textit{sunken} \text{ ship（沉船）} \\ = \text{a ship } \textit{which has sunk} \end{cases}$$

$$\begin{cases} \text{a } \textit{retired} \text{ officer（退役軍官）} \\ = \text{an officer } \textit{who has retired} \end{cases}$$ $$\begin{cases} \text{a } \textit{drunken} \text{ man（喝醉酒的人）} \\ = \text{a man } \textit{who is drunk} 【drunk 為 \textit{adj.}】 \end{cases}$$

【註】 比較下面現在分詞與過去分詞意義上的差別

(A) 大多數**及物動詞**的現在分詞和過去分詞**有主動、被動之分**

$$\begin{cases} \text{a } \textit{criticizing} \text{ speech（一個批評人的演講）} \\ = \text{a speech } \textit{which criticizes someone} \end{cases}$$

$$\begin{cases} \text{a } \textit{criticized} \text{ speech（一個受批評的演講）} \\ = \text{a speech } \textit{which is criticized by someone} \end{cases}$$

(B) **不及物動詞**的現在分詞和過去分詞則**有進行、完成之分**

$$\left\{ \begin{array}{l} \textbf{\textit{boiling}} \text{ water （正在沸騰的水）} \\ = \text{water } \textit{which is boiling} \end{array} \right.$$

$$\left\{ \begin{array}{l} \textbf{\textit{boiled}} \text{ water（已開過的水。可能是燙的，也可能是冷的）} \\ = \text{water } \textit{which has (been) boiled}【\text{boil 是及物和不及物兩用動詞}】 \end{array} \right.$$

a **_drowning_** man（快淹死的人）

a **_drowned_** man（已經淹死的人）

falling leaves（正在飄落的樹葉）

fallen leaves（已落在地上的樹葉）

(2) **分詞的位置：**

① **前位修飾**：分詞單獨修飾名詞時，原則上置於被修飾的名詞之前。

She opened the letter with **_trembling_** hands.（她用顫抖的手拆開那封信。）

He told us a very **_touching_** story.（他告訴我們一個很感人的故事。）

What are you planning to do in the **_coming_** vacation?

（在即將來臨的假期，你打算做些什麼？）

It is dangerous to swim in **_running_** water.（在急流中游泳很危險。）

Stolen fruit tastes sweet.（偷來的水果特別甜。）

There were some **_distinguished_** men among the guests.（來賓中有些知名之士。）

② **後位修飾**：下列情況，分詞該放在名詞後。

(A) **由若干個字所合成的分詞**（即完成式或被動語態）作形容詞用時，一定要置於被修飾的名詞的後面

Do you know who the boy **_being punished_** by our teacher is?

（你知不知道正被老師處罰的那個小男孩是誰？）

A person **_having failed_** once is very likely not to have the courage to try it again.

（失敗了一次的人很可能沒有勇氣再試了。）

(B) **做形容詞的分詞片語**（帶有受詞、補語或副詞的分詞）也必須放在被修飾的名詞的後面

Men **_living_** _in town_ do not know the pleasures of country life.

（住在城市的人不知道鄉村生活的樂趣。）

Nowadays we can, at home, listen to music **_played_** _in distant countries._

（現在我們能在家裡聽在遙遠的地方演奏的音樂了。）

He is a famous poet **_known_** _all over the world._（他是舉世聞名的詩人。）

(C) 如果被修飾的字是由 "**some (any, no) + thing (body, one)**" 所形成的不定代名詞或**指示代名詞 those 時**，雖然是一個單一的分詞作形容詞用，也要放在被修飾字的後面

Let me tell you _something_ **_interesting_**.（我來告訴你一件有趣的事情。）

Among _those_ **_invited_** were some ladies.（被邀請的人當中有些是女士。）

(D) 有時為了**強調**也可將單一的分詞置於被修飾的名詞之後

Money **_lent_** is money **_spent_**.（錢借出去就等於花掉了。）【重點在 lent 和 spent】

【比較】

Lent money is **_spent_** money.（借出去的錢等於花掉的錢。）【重點在 money】

(3) **分詞可造成複合形容詞**：分詞常與其他字結合，仍作形容詞用，以連字號（hyphen）"-"連接。

① 由「**副詞 + 過去分詞**」而形成的複合形容詞，其關係相當於形容詞子句的動詞與副詞。

> a *beautifully-dressed* woman（衣著華麗的女人）
> = a woman *who dresses beautifully*

> a *well-behaved* child（守規矩的小孩）
> = a child *who behaves well*

> a *much-praised* man（備受稱讚的人）
> = a man *who is praised much*

> the *above-mentioned* facts（上述的事實）
> = the facts *mentioned above*

② 由「**形容詞 + 過去分詞**」而形成的複合形容詞，其關係通常相當於形容詞子句的動詞與補語。

> a *ready-made* dress（現成的衣服；成衣）
> = a dress *which is already made*

> a *high-born* child（出身高貴的小孩）
> = a child *who was born high*
> = a child *of high birth*

> *green-painted* houses（漆成綠色的房子）
> = houses *which are painted green*

> a *plain-spoken* man（說話坦白的人）
> = a man *who is plain in speaking*

【注意】有時複合形容詞中的過去分詞之前附加形容詞或加上副詞時的意思相同。

> a *new-built* house = a *newly built* house（新建造的房子）
> a *new-laid* egg = a *newly laid* egg（剛下的蛋）

③ 由「**名詞 + 過去分詞**」所合成的複合形容詞，相當於形容詞子句的主詞與動詞的關係。

> a *man-made* fiber（人造纖維）
> = a fiber *made by man*

> a *Taiwan-raised* baseball player（台灣栽培出來的棒球選手）
> = a baseball player *raised in Taiwan*

> a *drought-stricken* area（遭受旱災的地區）
> = an area *which is stricken by drought*

④ 由「**名詞 + 現在分詞**」所合成的複合形容詞，相當於形容詞子句的動詞與受詞的關係。

> a *man-eating* beast（吃人的野獸）
> = a beast *which eats man*

> a *heart-rending* problem（令人心碎的問題）
> = a problem *that rends one's heart*

> a *self-sacrificing* act（自我犧牲的行為）
> = an act *by which one sacrifices oneself*

> a *blood-curdling* story（令人不寒而慄的故事）
> = a story *that curdles one's blood*

> *peace-loving* peoples（愛好和平的民族）
> = peoples *who love peace*

【比較】Spanish-speaking 和 spoken Spanish 的意義不同。

> *Spanish-speaking* peoples（說西班牙語的民族）
> = peoples *who speak Spanish*
>
> *spoken Spanish*（口說的西班牙語）【過去分詞做形容詞】
> （是 oral Spanish 的意思，和 written Spanish 相對）

⑤ 由「形容詞 + 現在分詞」所形成的複合形容詞，其關係相當於形容詞子句的動詞與補語。

　　a *silly-looking* person（傻裡傻氣的人）
　　= a person *who looks silly*

　　a *nice-looking* girl（漂亮的女孩）
　　= a girl *who is nice to look at*

　　a *sweet-smelling* rose（芳香的玫瑰）
　　= a rose *that smells sweet*

　　a *weak-sounding* heart（跳動微弱的心臟）
　　= a heart *that sounds weak*

　　an *easy-going* person（悠哉的人）
　　= a person *who is easygoing*

　　ill-fitting clothes（不合身的衣服）
　　= clothes *which fit poorly*

⑥ 由「副詞 +（不及物動詞的）現在分詞」所形成的複合形容詞。

　　far-reaching scheme（遠大的計劃）
　　on-coming tide（即將來臨的潮汐）
　　out-going plane（離去的飛機）
　　well-meaning advice（善意的忠告）

⑦ 由「形容詞（或名詞）+ 擬似分詞」所形成的複合形容詞。

　　在名詞字尾加 ed，可作形容詞用，表示「具有～」之意，此種形容詞稱為擬似分詞。

　　a *one-eyed* general（獨眼將軍）
　　= a general *with one eye*

　　a *kind-hearted* woman（好心腸的女人）
　　= a woman *with a kind heart*

　　a *chicken-hearted* fellow（膽小的傢伙）
　　= a fellow *with a chicken heart*

　　a *three-legged* table（三隻腳的桌子）
　　= a table *with three legs*

　　a *loose-tongued* fellow（隨口亂說的傢伙）
　　= a fellow *with a loose tongue*

　　a *smooth-tongued* fellow（花言巧語的傢伙）
　　= a fellow *with a smooth tongue*

　　a *honey-mouthed* fellow（甜言蜜語的傢伙）
　　= a fellow *with a honey mouth*

　　a *noble-minded* man（思想高尚的人）
　　= a man *with a noble mind*

{ a *narrow-minded* man（心胸狹窄的人）
= a man *with a narrow mind*

{ an *open-minded* person（心胸開闊的人）
= a person *with an open mind*

{ an *absent-minded* professor（健忘的教授）
= a professor *who is forgetful*

{ a *cool-headed* man（頭腦冷靜的人）
= a man *with a cool head*

{ a *clear-headed* man（頭腦清楚的人）
= a man *with a clear head*

{ a *hot-tempered* man（急性子的人）
= a man *with a hot temper*

{ a *good-tempered* man（好脾氣的人）
= a man *with a good temper*

{ a *bad-tempered* man（壞脾氣的人）
= a man *with a bad temper*

{ a *quick-sighted* man（眼光敏銳的人）
= a man *with a quick sight*

{ a *tender-skinned* girl（皮膚細緻的女孩）
= a girl *with a tender skin*

{ a *grey-haired* man（白髮的人）
= a man *with grey hair*

{ a *round-faced* girl（圓臉的女孩）
= a girl *with a round face*

{ a *bare-footed* boy（赤腳的小男孩）
= a boy *whose feet are bare*

{ a *good-mannered* child（有禮貌的小孩）
= a child *of good manners*

{ a *long-tailed* ape（長尾猿）
= an ape *with a long tail*

{ a *long-armed* monkey（長臂猴）
= a monkey *with long arms*

{ a *moderate-sized* room（大小適中的房間）
= a room *of moderate size*

{ a *five-roomed* house（有五個房間的房屋）
= a house *with five rooms*

{ a *smooth-surfaced* table（表面光滑的桌子）
= a table *with a smooth surface*

{ a *teen-aged* girl（十幾歲的女孩）
= a girl *in her teens*

3. **作補語用**：和形容詞一樣，分詞可做主詞補語和受詞補語。

　(1) **做主詞補語**：(參照 p.14)

　　① **主詞 + 不完全不及物動詞 + 現在分詞（主詞補語）**

　　　此句型具有進行、主動的意思，與句中主要動詞表示的動作同時在進行

　　　She *sat* up ***reading*** last night.（她昨晚熬夜讀書。）

　　　【reading 修飾 She，爲主詞補語。句中 reading 是與 sat 同時的動作】

　　　I *stood* ***leaning*** against a tree.（我靠著樹站著。）

　　　A soldier *lay* ***dying*** on the battlefield.（有個士兵躺在戰場上快要死了。）

　　　The boy *came* ***running*** to meet me.（那男孩跑來和我見面。）

　　　They *went* along ***singing*** merrily.（他們一面走一面高興地唱著歌。）

　　　The child *kept* ***crying*** all night.（那小孩整夜在哭。）

　　　He *remained* ***standing*** for an hour.（他持續站了一小時。）

　　　　【註1】　上述例句中 **sit, stand, lie** 表「位置」，**come, go** 表「行動」，**keep, remain** 表「連續」，都可以說是 be 動詞的變體。

　　　　【註2】　當然分詞可放在 be 動詞後做主詞補語，如：

　　　　　　　　This book is quite ***interesting***.（這本書很有趣。）

　　② **主詞 + 不完全不及物動詞 + 過去分詞（主詞補語）**

　　　此句型具有被動之意

　　　Many soldiers *lay* ***wounded***.（很多士兵受傷躺在地上。）

　　　【wounded 修飾 soldiers，爲主詞補語，表示被動】

　　　The child did not *grow* ***tired*** of hearing stories.（這小孩對聽故事一點也不厭倦。）

　　　I *felt* ***exhausted*** this morning.（我今天早上覺得筋疲力盡。）

　　　When did you *become* ***acquainted*** with him?（你何時認識他的？）

　　　He *stole* away ***unnoticed***.（沒人注意到他溜走了。）

　　③ **主詞 + 動詞（被動語態）+ 分詞（主詞補語）**

　　　The child *was found* ***sleeping*** in the bathroom.（這孩子被發現在浴室睡覺。）

　　　She *was heard* ***crying***.（有人聽到她在哭。）

　(2) **做受詞補語**：(參照 p.15)

　　① **主詞 + 不完全及物動詞 + 受詞 + 現在分詞（受詞補語）**

　　　此句型中的受詞即爲該分詞的意義主詞

　　　I *found* him ***lying*** on the grass.（我發現他躺在草地上。）【him 爲 lying 的意義主詞】

　　　I *watched* him ***painting*** the house.（我看他油漆房子。）

　　　The news *set* them ***crying***.（這消息使他們哭泣。）

　　　I *hear* a bird ***singing*** in the woods.（我聽到有隻鳥在林中唱歌。）

　　② **主詞 + 不完全及物動詞 + 受詞 + 過去分詞（受詞補語）**

　　　此句型中的受詞即爲該分詞的意義受詞

　　　I *had* my purse ***picked***.（我的錢包被扒了。）

　　　【picked 修飾 purse，而 purse 爲 picked 的意義受詞】

　　　I *had* my shoes ***mended***.（我把鞋子拿去修理。）

I *want* my shoes *mended*. (我要鞋子修理好。)

I *considered* this problem *settled*. (我認爲這個問題解決了。)

I *saw* the ground *covered* with snow. (我看到地上蓋滿了雪。)

He *found* a fox *concealed* behind the tree. (他發現一隻狐狸躲在樹後。)

【conceal oneself = be concealed 隱藏】

【註 1】 使役動詞 **have, make** 接過去分詞爲受詞補語表被動；接原形動詞表主動。

I will *have* my glasses *repaired*. (我會拿我的眼鏡去修理。)

I will *have* my friend *repair* my glasses. (我會要我的朋友修理我的眼鏡。)

【註 2】 **get, want, wish** 接過去分詞爲受詞補語，表示被動；接帶 **to** 的不定詞爲受詞補語時，表示主動。

She will *get* him *to mend* her fence. (她要他修理她的籬笆。)

She will *get* her fence *mended*. (她要請人修理她的籬笆。)

I *want* (*wish*) you *to finish* it by Friday. (我要你在星期五前完成它。)

I *want* (*wish*) it *finished* by Friday. (我要這件事在星期五前完成。)

【註 3】 感官動詞 **see, hear, watch** 接過去分詞表被動；接原形動詞或現在分詞表主動。

I *saw* him *beating* (*beat*) a cat. (我看見他在打貓。)

I *saw* a cat *being beaten* by him. (我看見一隻貓被他打。)

【因表示進行的意思，故用進行被動的分詞】

I *heard* him *shouting* (*shout*) in the room. (我聽見他在房間裡喊叫。)

I never *heard* him *spoken* ill of. (我從未聽過有人說他的壞話。)

I *watch* her *painting* (*paint*) the wall. (我看見她在油漆牆壁。)

I *watch* the wall *being painted* by her. (我看見牆被她油漆。)

【因表示進行的意思，故用進行被動的分詞】

4. **作名詞用**：分詞和形容詞一樣，前面加定冠詞 "the" 即可成爲名詞。一般情形表複數，亦有少數用法表單數，如：the condemned (被判罪的人)，the deceased (死者)，the accused (被告)；有時視其句意而定，如：the dying (瀕死的人)。

The departed was a friend of mine. (死者是我的朋友。)【單數】

The employers and *the employed* had a fine talk last night. 【複數】
(勞資雙方昨晚懇切地晤談了。)

The learned are most modest. (有學問的人都是非常謙虛的。)【複數】

The battlefield was full of *the dying* and *the wounded*. 【複數】
(戰場上到處都是瀕死的人和受傷的人。)

The dying murmured his last will weakly. (那臨死的人虛弱地說出他的遺囑。)【單數】

The unexpected has happened. (意料之外的事情已經發生了。)【單數】

The unknown has a mysterious attraction. (未知的事物都有一種神秘的吸引力。)【單數】

He was at present *the* most *admired* of them. (目前他是他們之中最令人佩服的人。)【單數】

The accused was acquitted yesterday. (被告昨天被宣判無罪。)【單數】

We mourned for *the deceased*. (我們爲死者哀悼。)【單數】

The condemned stood there dazedly. (那被判有罪的人恍惚地站在那裡。)【單數】

【例外】極少數分詞可不加定冠詞，或加 s, es 來表示複數。

Dead and *dying* were lying about.（已死和快死的人到處橫臥著。）

Let *bygones* be *bygones*.（讓過去的事過去吧；既往不咎。）

5. **作副詞用**：少數現在分詞可當副詞用，以加深形容詞的程度或狀態，相當於「**極度；非常；很**」之意，但比 very 稍強一點。此種當副詞用的分詞均可加 ly，但加 ly 較少用。

There have been several
- *boiling*（= *boilingly*）
- *burning*（= *burningly*）
- *steaming*（'stimɪŋ）
- *scalding*（'skɔldɪŋ）
- *scorching*（'skɔrtʃɪŋ）
- *piping*（'paɪpɪŋ）

hot days this month.

（這個月已經有幾天酷熱的日子。）【括弧內的分詞與 hot 連用，表「非常熱；酷熱」】

It was
- *freezing*（'frizɪŋ）
- *biting*（'baɪtɪŋ）
- *perishing*（'pɛrɪʃɪŋ）
- *piercing*（'pɪrsɪŋ）

cold yesterday.（昨天寒冷刺骨。）

【括弧內的分詞與 cold 連用，表「非常冷；寒冷刺骨」】

We got
- *drenching*（'drɛntʃɪŋ）
- *dripping*（'drɪpɪŋ）
- *soaking*（'sokɪŋ）
- *sopping*（'sɑpɪŋ）

wet on the way.（我們在路上被雨淋成落湯雞了。）

【括弧內的分詞與 wet 連用，表「濕透；浸透」】

He has a
- *thundering*（'θʌndərɪŋ）
- *shocking*（'ʃɑkɪŋ）

bad temper.（他有火爆的脾氣。）

【括弧內的分詞與 bad 連用，表「非常壞的」】

His tie was *staring*（（'stɛrɪŋ）刺眼地）red.（他的領帶是鮮紅色的。）

We're having a *ripping*（'rɪpɪŋ）good time.（我們正玩得很愉快。）【ripping good 非常好】

【註】amazing, exceeding, surprising 等字做副詞時容易造成誤解，因此**通常都用 -ly 的形式做副詞**，比較下列句子，同樣的句子，可作不同的解釋：

I met an *amazing* tall girl this morning.（今天早上我遇到一位高得驚人的女孩。）

I met an *amazing* tall girl this morning.（今天早上我遇到一位驚人的高女孩。）

6. **作介詞用**：下面各例中的分詞因其功用和介詞一樣，所以已被認為是介詞，不再被認為是分詞了。

Considering his age, he looks very young.
= *For* his age, he looks very young.（以他的年齡而論，他顯得非常年輕。）

Owing to his illness, he was absent.（他因病缺席。）
= *Because of* his illness, he was absent.
= *On account of* his illness, he was absent.

Regarding his plan, I don't know it at all. (關於他的計劃，我一無所知。)
= *Concerning* his plan, I don't know it at all.
= *Respecting* his plan, I don't know it at all.
= *Touching* his plan, I don't know it at all.
= *As for* his plan, I don't know it at all.
= *With regard to* his plan, I don't know it at all.

Ten persons got hurt, *including* the driver. (有十個人受傷，包括司機在內。)
= Ten persons got hurt, *inclusive of* the driver.
= Ten persons got hurt, the driver *included*.

Ten persons escaped, *excluding* the captain. (有十個人逃走，隊長不包括在內。)
= Ten persons escaped, *exclusive of* the captain.
= Ten persons escaped, the captain *excluded*.

According to the newspapers, he would resign soon. (根據報紙上說，他很快就會辭職。)

Notwithstanding his wealth, he is not content. 【*notwithstanding* = *in spite of*】
(儘管他很富有，他並不滿足。)

He refused to go near anyone *saving* his father. 【*saving* = *save* = *except*】
(除了他的父親，他拒絕接近任何人。)

Pending the trial, he was kept in prison. (在審判期間，他被關在監獄裡。) 【*pending* = *during*】

We shall arrive at noon *barring* accidents. 【*barring* = *bar* = *except*】
(除非有意外，否則我們將於中午到達。)

She is *past* sixty. (她年過六十歲。)【past 是由 pass 之過去分詞轉變而來】
It is half *past* ten o'clock. (現在是十點半。)
He rushed *past* me. (他匆匆忙忙走過我身邊。)

Excepting this one, they are all right. (除了這個以外，其餘都可以。)

【註】excepting 和 except 同義，但**在句首或在 not, without, always 之後只用 excepting**，不用 except。(參照 p.570)

Everyone, not { *except*【誤】 / *excepting*【正】 } myself, must share the blame.
(每個人都該受責備，我自己也不例外。)

7. **作連接詞用：**下列各例句中的分詞，因其功用和連接詞一樣，已被認為是連接詞，不再被認為是分詞。

Granting (*that*) this is true, you are still in the wrong. (即使這是真的，你還是錯的。)
= *Granted* (*that*) this is true, you are still in the wrong.
= *Admitting* (*that*) this is true, you are still in the wrong.
= *If we grant that* this is true, you are still in the wrong.
= *Though we grant that* this is true, you are still in the wrong.

Seeing (*that*) you love her so much, why don't you marry her?
= *Considering* (*that*) you love her so much, why don't you marry her?
= *Now* (*that*) you love her so much, why don't you marry her?
= *Since* you love her so much, why don't you marry her? (既然你如此愛她，為什麼不娶她？)

$\begin{cases} \textit{Supposing (\textbf{that})} \text{ the earth were flat, what would happen?} \\ = \textbf{Suppose (\textit{that})} \text{ the earth were flat, what would happen?} 【不可用 \textit{Supposed}】 \\ = \textbf{Providing (\textit{that})} \text{ the earth were flat, what would happen?} \\ = \textbf{Provided (\textit{that})} \text{ the earth were flat, what would happen?} \\ = \textit{If} \text{ the earth were flat, what would happen?} （如果地球是平的，會發生什麼事？） \end{cases}$

He is honest, ***notwithstanding*** (***that***) he is poor. 【***notwithstanding*** (***that***) = *although*】
（他雖然貧窮，卻很誠實。）

V. 分詞構句：

(I) **分詞片語與分詞構句**：為了文法上解釋的便利，大多數文法家把分詞帶頭的片語分類為<u>分詞片語</u>和<u>分詞構句</u>。

1. **分詞片語有限定作用**，只能放在其所修飾的名詞之後以修飾該名詞，不能用逗點分開，意義上和限定用法的形容詞子句一樣。（參照 p.162 限定用法和補述用法形容詞子句的比較）

   └── 分 詞 片 語 ──┐
   The girl ***playing the piano*** did not know it.
   = The girl *who was playing the piano* did not know it.

2. **分詞構句沒有限定作用**，通常放在主詞之前，或主詞與動詞之間，**要用逗點分開。分詞構句可能是補述用法的形容詞子句簡化而來，也可能是副詞子句簡化而來**，表示**時間、原因、理由、條件、讓步、連續或附帶狀態**等。看下面句子的兩種解釋，可知分詞構句可能同時具有形容詞片語和副詞片語的雙重性質。

   $\begin{cases} \text{The girl, \textbf{\textit{playing the piano}}, did not know it. （正在彈鋼琴的那個女孩不知道那件事。）} \\ = \text{The girl, \textit{who was playing the piano}, did not know it.} \end{cases}$

   $\begin{cases} \text{The girl, \textbf{\textit{playing the piano}}, did not know it.} \\ \text{（那個女孩因正在彈鋼琴，所以不知道那件事。）} \\ = \textbf{\textit{Playing the piano}}, \text{ the girl did not know it.} \\ = \textit{As the girl was playing the piano}, \text{ she did not know it.} \end{cases}$

   分詞構句可改變成合句的一個對等子句，和原句主要子句並立。

   $\begin{cases} \text{She said goodbye, \textbf{\textit{waving her hand}}. （她說聲再見，並揮揮手。）} \\ = \text{She said goodbye \textit{and waved her hand}.} \end{cases}$

   $\begin{cases} \text{She sat by the window, \textbf{\textit{looking at the snow scene outside}}.} \\ \text{（她坐在窗邊看著外面的雪景。）} \\ = \text{She sat by the window \textit{and looked at the snow scene outside}.} \end{cases}$

(II) **子句和分詞片語、分詞構句的轉換**

1. **形容詞子句改為分詞片語的方法：**

   (1) 若關係代名詞之後有 be 動詞，則刪去關係代名詞和 be 動詞即成分詞片語。

   $\begin{cases} \text{Watch the man \textit{who is coming this way}. （注意朝這邊來的那個人。）} \\ = \text{Watch the man \textbf{\textit{coming this way}}.} \end{cases}$

   $\begin{cases} \text{Lessons \textit{which are learned easily} are soon forgotten.} \\ \text{（容易學習的功課很快就會忘了。）} \\ = \text{Lessons \textbf{\textit{learned easily}} are soon forgotten.} \end{cases}$

(2) 若關係代名詞之後沒有 be 動詞而爲一般動詞，則刪去關係代名詞，再將動詞改爲現在分詞。

> Anyone *who wishes to leave early* may do so.
> = Anyone ***wishing to leave early*** may do so.
> （任何人想要早一點離開的都可以離開。）

> The building *which belongs to my uncle* stands on the corner of that street.
> = The building ***belonging to my uncle*** stands on the corner of that street.
> （屬於我叔叔的那棟建築物就在那條街的轉角處。）

2. 副詞子句改爲分詞構句的方法：

> (1) 先將引導副詞子句的連接詞去掉。
> (2) 副詞子句的主詞與主要子句的主詞相同時，則再把副詞子句的主詞去掉；如不相同時則保留。
> (3) 任何動詞（包括 be 動詞）均改爲現在分詞。（如進行式，則須把 be 動詞去掉）
> (4) 分詞爲 being 和 having been 時，可把它省略掉。
> (5) 如遇到否定詞則放在分詞前（否定詞＋分詞）。
> (6) 其餘照抄。

前後主詞相同的情況

> *After I had seen my brother*, I felt much relieved. （見到哥哥之後，我覺得放心多了。）
> = ***Having** seen my brother*, I felt much relieved.

> *As he is ill*, he cannot attend the meeting. （他因病不能參加會議。）
> = ***Being** ill*, he cannot attend the meeting.

> *If you turn to the right*, you will find the bank. （如果你向右轉，就會找到銀行。）
> = ***Turning** to the right*, you will find the bank.

> *When he was buying the book*, he met an old friend.
> = ***Buying** the book*, he met an old friend. （他買書的時候，遇見一位老朋友。）

> *As he has been praised too much*, he becomes too proud.
> = (***Having been***) *praised too much*, he becomes too proud.
> （因爲他受到過份的誇獎，而變得驕傲。）

> *Though he hadn't found his key*, he still had the money with him.
> = ***Not having** found his key*, he still had the money with him.
> （雖然他沒找到鑰匙，他仍有錢帶在身上。）

前後主詞不相同的情況（帶有意義上主詞的分詞片語，稱爲**獨立分詞構句**，因爲這種片語不可能來自補述用法的形容詞子句，與主要子句主詞無關，故稱之獨立分詞構句。）

> *After the sun had set*, we arrived at the station. （我們在太陽下山後抵達車站。）
> = *The sun **having** set*, we arrived at the station.

> *When school was over*, the boys went home. （放學了，男孩們就回家了。）
> = *School **being** over*, the boys went home.

> *As my homework has been done*, I have nothing else to do.
> = *My homework* (***being***) *done*, I have nothing else to do.
> （因爲我的作業寫完了，所以我沒有別的事做。）

【註 1】 若副詞子句的主詞爲人稱代名詞（We, You, He, I 等）時，雖然和主要子句的主詞不同，分詞片語的主詞也可以省略，此分詞片語當然也稱爲**獨立分詞構句**。

> *If we speak strictly*, you are not justified.（嚴格說起來，你沒有充分的理由。）
> = (*We*) *Strictly speaking*, you are not justified.

> *If we take all things into consideration*, he is an honorable man.
> = (*We*) *Taking all things into consideration*, he is an honorable man.
> （從各方面來說，他是個可敬的人。）

【註 2】 副詞子句改爲分詞構句時，若主要子句的動詞爲現在式，副詞子句的動詞爲過去式，而爲了要表示副詞子句的動詞動作時間早於主要子句的動詞應改爲**完成式分詞**，表示**比主要子句動詞的動作先發生**。

> *As he was idle in his youth*, he has to work hard in his old age.
> = (*Having been*) *idle in his youth*, he has to work hard in his old age.
> （他因爲年輕的時候遊手好閒，現在年老的時候必須努力工作。）

> *As this book was printed in haste*, it has many misprints.
> = (*Having been*) *printed in haste*, this book has many misprints.
> （本書因倉促付印，印刷錯誤的地方很多。）

3. **對等子句改爲分詞構句的方法**：分詞構句可代替合句中的另一對等子句，其作用是說話者對主要子句的敘述加以補充說明。

(1) **對等子句主詞相同時**，保留一主詞即可，即 **and（＋主詞）＋ V ＝ ～ing**

> My train starts at twelve, *and* (*it*) *will arrive at Taipei at three.*
> = My train starts at twelve, *arriving* at Taipei at three.
> （我搭的火車十二點開，將於三點鐘抵達台北。）

> She alone remained at home, *and* (*she*) *cleaned the rooms and washed clothes.*
> = She alone remained at home, *cleaning* the rooms and *washing* clothes.
> （她一個人留在家裡，並且清掃房間和洗衣服。）

(2) **對等子句主詞不同時**，改爲獨立分詞構句，兩個主詞都保留。

> He was reading a book, *and his wife was knitting beside him.*
> = He was reading a book, *his wife knitting beside him.*
> （他在看書，他太太在他旁邊編織。）

> They were still in the room, *and tears ran down their cheeks.*
> = They were still in the room, *tears running down their cheeks.*
> （他們還在房間裡，並且淚流滿面。）

(3) **分詞構句亦可代替第一個對等子句**，但必須放在主詞前面。

> *I walked on tiptoe, and* approached the window.（我踮腳尖悄悄地走近窗戶。）
> = *Walking on tiptoe*, I approached the window.

> *He looked up at his father, and* asked what was the matter with him.
> = *Looking up at his father*, he asked what was the matter with him.
> （他抬頭看著他的父親，問說他怎麼了。）

(Ⅲ) 分詞構句的含意：<u>分詞構句可從上下文判斷出有下列各種不同的意義。</u>

1. 表時間：相當於 **when**, **as**, **while**, **as soon as**, **after** 等所引導的副詞子句

> *Hearing the news*, they all danced for joy. (聽到這消息，他們高興得跳起舞來。)
> = *When they heard the news*, they all danced for joy.

> *Seeing the cat*, the mouse ran off. (一見到貓，老鼠就跑了。)
> = *As soon as the mouse saw the cat*, it ran off.

2. 表原因、理由：相當於 **as**, **because** 等所引導的副詞子句

> *Being sick*, I was absent from school yesterday. (因為生病，我昨天沒去上學。)
> = *Since I was sick*, I was absent from school yesterday.

> *Having been idle in his youth*, he has to work hard in his old age.
> = *As he was idle in his youth*, he has to work hard in his old age.
> (他因為年輕時遊手好閒，年老就必須辛苦工作。)

3. 表條件：等於 **if**, **unless** 等所引導的副詞子句

> *United*, we stand; *divided*, we fall. (團結則立，分散則倒。)
> = *Being united*, we stand; *being divided*, we fall.
> = *If we are united*, we stand; *if we are divided*, we fall.

> *Exercising every morning*, you will improve your health.
> = *If you exercise every morning*, you will improve your health.
> (如果每天運動，就能改善你的健康。)

4. 表讓步：相當於 **though**, **although** 等所引導的副詞子句

> *Wounded*, the brave soldier continued to fight.
> = *Though he was wounded*, the brave soldier continued to fight.
> (雖然受傷，那勇敢的士兵還繼續作戰。)

> *Admitting what you say*, I still think you are wrong.
> = *Though I admit what you say*, I still think you are wrong.
> (雖然我承認你所說的話是真的，但我仍然認為你不對。)

5. 表連續或附帶狀態：表示連續的兩個動作或附帶說明事情

> My train starts at six, *arriving there at four p.m.* 【表連續】
> = My train starts at six, *and (it) will arrive there at four p.m.*
> (我的火車六點開，下午四點到那裡。)

> In 1920 he went to London, *living there till his death*. 【表連續】
> = In 1920 he went to London, *and (he) lived there till his death*.
> (1920 年他去倫敦，就住在那裡一直到死。)

> His father died, *leaving nothing but a lot of debt*. 【表附帶狀態】
> = His father died, *and (he) left nothing but a lot of debt*.
> (他的父親去世了，除了很多債務外，什麼也沒有留下。)

> She wrote him a friendly letter, *thanking him for his help and sending him her best wishes*.
> = She wrote him a friendly letter, *and thanked him for his help and sent him her best wishes*.
> (她寫了一封親切的信給他，感謝他的幫助，並且祝福他。)【表附帶狀態】

(IV) **分詞構句的位置**：分詞構句可置於①**句首**②**句中**（主詞之後）③**句尾**，不過都要**用逗點分隔**。

> *Crying for milk*, the baby woke everyone up. （小嬰兒哭著要吃奶，把每個人都吵醒了。）
> = The baby, *crying for milk*, woke everyone up.
> = The baby woke everyone up, *crying for milk*.
>
> *Being very tired*, the girl lay down on the grass. （由於很疲倦，那女孩躺在草地上。）
> = The girl, *being very tired*, lay down on the grass.
> = The girl lay down on the grass, *being very tired*.

【註】 **主詞是人稱代名詞時**，分詞構句只可放在句首或句尾，但**不可放在主詞**（人稱代名詞）**之後。**

　　Being ill, he could not attend the meeting. （他因病不能出席會議。）【正】

　　He, *being ill*, could not attend the meeting. 【誤】

　　I went to see Tom, *finding him absent*. （我去拜訪湯姆，但發現他不在。）【正】

　　I, *finding him absent*, went to see Tom. 【誤】

但在第二個對等子句裡，主詞雖然是代名詞，為了句意明確起見，可將分詞構句置於代名詞後。

　　Everyone seemed to be talking, and I, *sitting in silence*, felt awkward.
　　（每個人都好像在談話，而我，靜靜地坐著，覺得很不自在。）

(V) **分詞構句之時式**

1. **簡單式的分詞構句**表示與句子的動詞發生在**相同的時間或略早些**。

　　Living in the suburbs, I have few visitors. （因為我住在郊外，幾乎沒有什麼訪客。）

> *Walking* along the street, he found a wallet. （他在街上走的時候，發現了一個皮夾。）
> = *While he was walking along the street*, he found a wallet.
>
> *Turning* the corner, the thief met a policeman face to face.
> = *When the thief turned the corner*, he met a policeman face to face.
> （那個小偷轉過街角的時候，面對面地遇到一個警察。）

【註】 如果分詞構句的時間觀念**遲於**主要動詞，則通常將分詞構句放在**句尾**，但仍然要用逗點分開。

> *Finding the door locked*, I went home. （發現門鎖著，我就回家了。）
> I went home, *finding the door locked*. （我回到家裡發現門鎖著。）

2. **完成式的分詞**所表示的時間比主要子句的動詞早完成。

> *Having lived* in America, he is proficient in English. （因為他住在美國，所以精通英文。）
> = *As he has lived in America*, he is proficient in English.
>
> *Having finished* his work, he took a rest. （因為他已做完工作，所以就休息一下。）
> = *As he had finished his work*, he took a rest.

(VI) **分詞構句的語態**

1. **主動的**：主動意義時用主動語態

　　Writing something on a card, he gave it to me. （他在卡片上寫了些東西，然後交給了我。）

Having written my composition, I have nothing more to do.
（我已寫完了作文，所以再也沒有事可做了。）

Having been writing letters all the morning, I had no time to attend to other matters.
（我寫了一早上的信，所以沒有時間專心做其他的事。）

2. 被動的：被動意義時，用被動語態，被動語態中的 **being 或 having been 可省略**

> The book, (*being*) *written* in an easy style, has many readers.
> = (*Being*) *written* in an easy style, the book has many readers.
> （這本書以淺易的文筆寫成，所以有很多讀者。）

> The book, (*having been*) *written* in haste, has many mistakes.
> = (*Having been*) *written* in haste, the book has many mistakes.
> （這書因倉促寫成，所以有很多錯誤。）

(VII) **連接詞 + 分詞**：此種句型，實際上是從屬連接詞 when, while, though 等，後省略了句意明確的主詞和 be 動詞而來的。(詳見 p.645)

> *While fighting* in Korea, he was taken prisoner. （在韓國作戰時，他被俘虜了。）
> = While *he was* fighting in Korea, he was taken prisoner.

> He will do better *if* properly *encouraged*. （如果受到適當的鼓勵，他會做得更好。）
> = He will do better if *he is* properly encouraged.

(VIII) **獨立分詞構句**：當分詞構句的意義上的主詞，不是句子的主詞時，必須在分詞構句前保留意義上的主詞，此種帶有意義主詞的分詞結構與主要子句主詞無文法關聯，所以稱為獨立分詞構句。比較下面兩句：

<u>Being ill in bed</u>, I cannot go to school. （我因為臥病在床，所以不能去上學。）
　　分詞構句

<u>Mother being ill in bed</u>, I cannot go to school. （我因為母親臥病在床，所以不能去上學。）
　　　獨立分詞構句

獨立分詞構句的含義和分詞構句相同，也可表時間、理由、條件、附帶狀態等。

> *The agent being absent*, the business was suspended. 【表原因】
> = *Since the agent was absent*, the business was suspended. (代理人缺席，所以生意暫停。)

> *Night coming on*, we sought shelter in a farmhouse. 【表時間】
> = *When night came on*, we sought shelter in a farmhouse.
> （夜晚來臨，我們投宿在一家農舍。）

> *Weather permitting*, I shall start tomorrow. 【表條件】
> = *If weather permits*, I shall start tomorrow. （如果天氣許可，我明天將要啟程。）

> He lay on the grass, (*with*) *the sun shining upon his face*. 【表附帶狀態】
> = He lay on the grass, *and the sun was shining upon his face*.
> （他躺在草地上，太陽照在他臉上。）

【註 1】 **表示附帶狀態的獨立分詞構句**，有時在其前面加上 with 或 without 而成「**with (*or* without) + 受詞 + ～ing**」的形式出現。**being** 省略後又演變成「**with (*or* without) + 受詞 + p.p. 或形容詞**」的形式。

> He lay still on the grass, *with his eyes* (*being*) *closed*.
> = He lay still on the grass, *and his eyes were closed*.
> （他靜靜地躺在草地上，雙眼緊閉著。）【及物動詞「非人」當主詞時要用被動】

He went angrily away, *without a word spoken*.
= He went angrily away, *and not a word was spoken*.
（他很生氣地走開，一句話也沒說。）

The old man sat reading, *with his dog sleeping beside him*.
= The old man sat reading, *and his dog was sleeping beside him*.
（那老人坐著看書，他的狗睡在他旁邊。）

She sat under a tree, *with her elbow resting on her knee*.
= She sat under a tree, *and her elbow rested on her knee*.
（她坐在樹下，把手肘放在膝蓋上。）

He was left alone in the empty house, *with hands* (*being*) *tied and mouth* (*being*) *gagged*.
= He was left alone in the empty house, *and his hands were tied and his mouth was gagged*.
（他被單獨留在空屋裡，手被綁住，嘴巴被貼住。）

He sat in the chair, *with his mouth* (*being*) *open*. （他就坐在椅子上，嘴巴張得開開的。）
I can't see *with you standing there*. （你站在那裡擋住我的視線。）

【註2】有些獨立分詞意義上的主詞表示「**一般人**」，如 **we**, **one**, **you** 時，**主詞可以省略**，稱為「**非人稱獨立分詞構句**」。（獨立分詞構句，不以主要子句的主詞為其意義主詞。）

Generally speaking, the climate of Taiwan is mild all the year round.
= *If we speak generally*, the climate of Taiwan is mild all the year round.
（一般說來，台灣的氣候整年都很溫和。）

Strictly speaking, the subject belongs to rhetoric.
= *If we speak strictly*, the subject belongs to rhetoric.
（嚴格地說來，這個主題是屬於修辭學。）

Judging from his look, he must be sick. （從他面容看來，他一定是生病了。）
= *If we judge from his look*, he must be sick.

Taking all things into consideration, he is an honorable man.
= *If we take all things into consideration*, he is an honorable man.
（從各方面來說，他是一個可敬的人。）

Talking of submarines, have you seen one? （說到潛水艇，你可曾見過？）
= *Now that we are talking of submarines*, have you seen one?

【類例】

speaking of ～（談到～）	calculating roughly（大致算來）
comparatively speaking（比較而言）	calculating strictly（嚴格算來）
frankly speaking（坦白說）	summing up（概括地說）
roughly speaking（大致說來）	properly speaking（正確地說）

請立刻做　練習一～八

第九篇　連接詞（Conjunctions）

第一章　概　論

I. 定義： 用來連接單字、片語、子句或句子的詞類稱爲**連接詞**；如果被連接的單字、片語、子句或句子在文法上佔同等地位，就稱之爲**對等連接詞**（Coordinate Conjunctions）；如果所引導的子句是從屬子句（包括：名詞子句、形容詞子句、副詞子句），而將主要子句和從屬子句連接起來成爲一個複合句，則稱之爲**從屬連接詞**（Subordinate Conjunctions）。

II. 種類：

連接詞

1. 按形式分
   - (1) **單一連接詞**（Simple Conjunctions）
     是由一個字形成的連接詞，如 and, but, if, than, that, although, because, therefore,…等。
   - (2) **片語連接詞**（Phrase Conjunctions）
     是具有連接詞作用的片語，即片語連接詞的功用相當於連接詞，如 as if, as well as, in case, in order that, for fear (that),…等。
   - (3) **相關連接詞**（Correlative Conjunctions）
     是一對分開的詞語，具有連接詞的作用，在句子中前後相互呼應，如 both…and, either…or, neither…nor, not only…but (also), as…as, so…as, so…that, whether…or, the…the,…等。

2. 按功用分
   - (1) **對等連接詞**（Coordinate Conjunctions）
     - ① 累積連接詞："and" 型（Cumulative Conjunctions）
     - ② 反義連接詞："but" 型（Adversative Conjunctions）
     - ③ 選擇連接詞："or" 型（Alternative Conjunctions）
     - ④ 推理連接詞："so" 型（Illative Conjunctions）
     - ⑤ 解釋連接詞："for" 型（Explanatory Conjunctions）
   - (2) **從屬連接詞**（Subordinate Conjunctions）
     - ① 引導名詞子句的從屬連接詞
     - ② 引導形容詞子句的從屬連接詞
     - ③ 引導副詞子句的從屬連接詞

第二章 對等連接詞（Coordinate Conjunctions）

對等連接詞的作用是**連接文法作用相同的單字、片語或子句**。但所連接的成份未必都是單字，或都是片語，或都是子句。也可連接單字和片語，或片語和子句，或單字和子句，但文法作用必須相同，即必須是同當名詞用，或同當形容詞用，或同當副詞用，如：

Shall we go <u>now</u> *or* <u>when your father comes</u>?（我們現在去或是等你父親來時才去？）【同作副詞用】
副詞副詞子句

如果對等連接詞連接兩個子句時，**它前面有無逗點均可**，如句子長，可將逗點改爲分號（；）。（參閱 p.40）

I went to his house(,) and he came to mine.（我去他家，而他來我家。）

對等連接詞按其功用可分爲：<u>累積連接詞</u>、<u>反義連接詞</u>、<u>選擇連接詞</u>、<u>推理連接詞</u>及<u>解釋連接詞</u>等五種。

I. **累積連接詞（Cumulative Conjunctions）**：就是將所連接的各部分累加在一起，通常以 "and" 爲代表。

1. **and**：連接文法作用相同的單字、片語、子句或句子。

　⑴ 作「和；而且」解

　　Mother *and* father are away today.（爸爸和媽媽今天不在。）

　　A textbook must be instructive *and* interesting.（教科書一定要有教育性和趣味性。）

　　Colonel Smith went across the river *and* into the trees.
　　（史密斯上校穿過河流並進入樹林。）

　　John moved to New York, *and* Alice moved to Seattle.
　　（約翰搬去紐約，愛麗絲搬去西雅圖。）

　⑵ 三個以上的連接，**在每個後面加逗點，最後一字才加 and**。

　　Sam enjoys tennis, golf, *and* baseball.（山姆喜歡網球、高爾夫球，以及棒球。）

　　The book tells the story of an old man, of his young wife, *and* of their many problems
　　of adjustment.（本書敘述一個老人，和他年輕的太太，以及他們相互適應的很多問題。）

　　Who he was, why he married her, what their problems were, *and* how it all ended
　　happily, are told with all the skill of a good storyteller.

　　（他是誰、爲何和她結婚、他們的問題是些什麼，以及如何有個圓滿的結局，都被一個很有
　　技巧的說故事者敘述出來。）

　　【註】有時爲了表示緊湊、一氣呵成，會將 and 省略；有時爲表示一一列舉，而將所有
　　　　　的對等連接詞 and 或 or 全部列出。

　　　　　He is a wise, sympathetic, hard-working teacher.【and 省略】
　　　　　（他是個聰明、有同情心，而且認眞的老師。）

　　　　　You can go to Hualien by bus, *or* by boat, *or* by airplane; but I think it is more
　　　　　interesting to go by bus.【or 全部列出】
　　　　　（你去花蓮可以搭巴士，或者坐船，或者搭飛機；不過我認爲搭巴士去比較有趣。）

　⑶ **and 連接兩個物品被視爲一物或同一人有兩種身份時**，第二名詞不加冠詞，做主詞時，
　　用單數動詞。

　　Spaghetti *and* meat sauce *is* a favorite dish with our employees.
　　（義大利肉醬麵是我們員工最喜歡的食物。）

The candlestick *and* candle *sells* for one dollar. (燭台和蠟燭賣一塊錢。)

A needle *and* thread *was* found on the floor. (在地板上發現了一根穿著線的針。)

The poet *and* novelist *is* dead. (這位詩人兼小說家死了。)

⑷ **and** 有時連接兩個相同的字，表「漸漸」、「重複」或加強語氣。

The voice became fainter *and* fainter. (聲音變得越來越微弱了。)

They tried *and* tried, but they did not succeed. (他們一試再試，但沒成功。)

⑸ 祈使句之後接 **and** 有條件句的作用。(參照 p.360)

> Go straight on, *and* you will see the library. (如果你一直走，就會看到那間圖書館。)
> = *If* you go straight on, you will see the library.

> Persevere, *and* you will succeed. (如果你堅忍不拔，你就會成功。)
> = *If* you persevere, you will succeed.

> One more step, *and* you will be a dead man. (如果你再向前一步，你就會死。)
> = *If* you walk one more step, you will be a dead man.

⑹ **and** 可代替表「目的」的不定詞 (此用法多半把 and 放在 come, go, try 之後)。

> Come *and* see me. (來看我。)
> = Come to see me. 【在現代美語中，come 和 go 之後的 and 或 to 常省略，參照 p.419】

> May I go *and* play now? (我現在可以去玩嗎？)
> = May I go to play now?

> Try *and* do this exercise. (試做此練習。)
> = Try to do this exercise. 【try 後 and 或 to 不可省略】

⑺ 形容詞 + **and** 可代替副詞使用。

> How *nice and* cool it is in the swimming pool! (在游泳池裡好涼快啊！)
> = How *pleasantly* cool it is in the swimming pool!

> It was *good and* dark, so we started for home. (天已漆黑了，所以我們就動身回家。)
> = It was *quite* dark, so we started for home.

【類例】
nice and tired = *very* tired	*good and* cold = *very* cold
fine and tall = *very* tall	*big and* busy = *very* busy
rare and hungry = *very* hungry	

2. **both…and** (…兩者都)

連接兩個文法作用相同的單字、片語或子句，有強調兩者的語氣的作用。

He has *both* the time *and* the money to play polo. (他既有時間又有錢來玩馬球。)

Exercise is good *both* for body *and* for mind. (運動對身心都有益處。)

It was *both* cold *and* wet. (天氣既冷又潮濕。)

She *both* built *and* endowed the hospital. (她建造並資助那家醫院。)

【註】 **both…and**，與 **at once…and** 及 **equally…and** 同義。

This book is ⎰ *both* / *at once* / *equally* ⎱ interesting *and* instructive. (這本書既有趣，又有教育性。)

3. **not only⋯but (also)**（不但⋯而且⋯）

連接兩個文法作用相同的單字、片語或子句；如果連接兩個主詞時，**重點在第二個主詞，故動詞的數與後者一致。**

Not only you *but also* I **am** wrong.（不僅你錯了，連我也錯了。）

Success depends *not only* on talent *but also* on effort.

（成功不僅靠才能，也要靠努力。）

I respect him *not only* for what he has done, *but* for what he is.

（我尊敬他不僅是為了他所做的事，而且也是為了他的為人。）

He can *not only* read, *but also* write French.（他不僅能讀，也能寫法文。）

Not only did he make a promise, *but* he kept it.

（他不僅許下諾言，而且做到了。）

【註 1】由上面最後一個例句看來，為了加強語氣將 **not only** 置於句首時，一定要把 **be** 動詞或助動詞放在主詞前倒裝。

　　　　Not only is he dependable, *but also* he is trustworthy.

　　　　Not only is he dependable, *but* he is *also* trustworthy.

　　　　（他不僅可靠，而且值得信賴。）

【註 2】not only⋯but also 中的 **only** 可用 **merely** 代替，**also** 可以省略或用 **likewise** 代替，或者把 also 移至句尾。but 也可省略，有時 but also 都省略。

　　　　It is *not* $\left\{\begin{array}{c} \textbf{\textit{only}} \\ \textbf{\textit{merely}} \end{array}\right\}$ heavy, *but* $\left\{\begin{array}{c} \textbf{\textit{also}} \\ \textbf{\textit{likewise}} \end{array}\right\}$ rough.（它不僅重，而且粗糙。）

　　　　He is *not only* a scholar *but* a statesman.【also 省略】

　　　　（他不僅是個學者，也是個政治家。）

　　　　It is *not only* interesting, *but* instructive *also*.

　　　　（這不僅有趣，而且有教育性。）

　　　　Not only is it difficult, it is impracticable *also*.【but 省略】

　　　　（這不僅困難，而且是無法實行的。）

　　　　This book is *not only* good, it is *also* cheap.【but 省略】

　　　　（這本書不只是好，而且便宜。）

　　　　She was *not only* compelled to stay at home, she was forbidden to see her friends.

　　　　（她不但被迫留在家裡，而且被禁止見她的朋友。）【but, also 都省略】

4. **as well as**（和⋯一樣；以及）

連接兩個文法作用相同的單字、片語或子句，如果連接兩個主詞時，重點放在前面，故**動詞的數與前面主詞一致。**

The teacher *as well as* the students *is* expected to study hard.

（老師和學生一樣應該用功讀書。）

He gave me money *as well as* advice.（他給我錢，也給我忠告。）

【註 1】**no less than = as well as**

　　　　Your friends, *no less than I*, *are* anxious to meet you.

　　　　（你的朋友和我一樣急著想和你見面。）

【註 2 】 **A, B, C 用 as well as 連接時**，不說 "*A, B, as well as C*"，**應該用 "A and B as well as C"**。

He plays basketball, football *as well as* baseball.【誤】
He plays basketball *and* football *as well as* baseball.【正】
（他打籃球，踢足球，也打棒球。）

【註 3 】 **A as well as B 可改爲 B and A as well**，但由於連接的部分重點有前後不同，所以 **A 與 B 的位置須調換**。

He has experience *as well as* scholarship.
= He has scholarship *and* experience *as well*.
（他有學問，也有經驗。）

【註 4 】 **不可用 both…as well as 代替 both…and**。

This news was *both* a joy $\begin{cases} as\ well\ as\ 【誤】 \\ and\ 【正】 \end{cases}$ a perplexity.

（這消息令人快樂，也令人困惑。）

5. **neither; nor**

⑴ **neither…nor 如果連接兩個主詞時，動詞的數與後者一致**。

Neither Tom *nor* I *am* going to attend the meeting.
（湯姆和我都不會去參加會議。）
I can *neither* read *nor* write. （我既不能讀，也不能寫。）
= I can't read *nor* write.

⑵ **nor** = (and) not…either（用於**否定子句之後**）。nor 放在句首，助動詞和 be 動詞要放在主詞前面，且第二個子句與前面相同的部分可以省略。nor 之前用分號或逗點皆可。

I can not lift the table, *nor* can you. （我不能舉起那桌子，你也不能。）
【本句是 you 之後省略 lift the table 而來】
He did not speak to me; *nor* did he give me anything.
（他不和我講話，也不給我任何東西。）
He sat silent, *nor* did I speak a word. （他沉默地坐著，我也不發一語。）
You are not a teacher, *nor* am I. （你不是老師，我也不是。）
It is not found in China *nor* in America.
（它不是在中國，也不是在美國找到的。）

【註 1 】 nor 前面也可加 and 或 but。

He does not do it, $\begin{cases} nor \\ and\ nor \\ but\ nor \end{cases}$ does he try to. （他不做那件事，也不試著去做。）

【註 2 】 nor 是連接詞，neither 是副詞性連接詞，因此 neither 接子句時，前面必須有分號、句點或 and。neither 做連接詞（ = nor ）是古老的用法，應該避免使用。

He is not wrong, *and neither* are you. （他沒有錯，你也沒有錯。）
You are not going, *and neither* am I. （你不去我也不去。）

6. $\begin{cases} \textbf{what with}\cdots, \textbf{and (what with)}\cdots（半因\cdots，半因\cdots）【表原因】\\ \textbf{what by}\cdots, \textbf{and (what by)}\cdots（半靠\cdots，半靠\cdots）【表手段】\\ \textbf{partly}\cdots\textbf{(and) partly}\cdots（部分\cdots，部分\cdots）【通常第二個 partly 之前有 and 或是逗點】\end{cases}$

What with overwork *and (what with)* undernourishment, he fell ill.
（一方面由於工作過度，一方面由於營養不良，他就生病了。）

What by scolding *and what by* coaxing, I barely managed to stop the child's crying.
（半靠責罵，半靠哄騙，我總算能叫那孩子不哭了。）

The letter was written *partly* in French *and partly* in English.
（這封信部分是用法文寫的，部分是用英文寫的。）

7. **副詞性連接詞（準連接詞）**：具有副詞的作用，但意義上卻與連接詞相同，**這些連接詞不能用來連接單字或片語**，只能用於連接子句或句子，表累積、連接的有：**besides, moreover, furthermore, further, in addition, also, likewise, similarly, indeed, again** 等，這些副詞連接詞的前面**通常有分號或句點**。

It's too late to go for a walk now; *besides*, it's beginning to rain.
（現在散步太晚了；何況又開始下雨了。）

I believe you understand what this project means to us. *Moreover*, I hope you will carry out the orders discreetly and faithfully.
（我想你了解這計劃對我們的意義。此外，我希望你會謹慎而忠實地完成這些命令。）

He has a good education; *moreover*, he is a genius.（他受過良好的教育；而且他是一位天才。）

Television is entertaining; *furthermore*, it is instructive.
（電視除了有娛樂性之外，還有教育性。）

You need money and time. *In addition*, you need diligence.
（你需要錢和時間。此外，你還需要勤勉。）

I prepared my English lesson; *also*, I wrote my French composition.
（我準備了我的英文課，也寫了我的法文作文。）

All of Mr. Jones' ancestors were sturdy and long-lived; *likewise*, he is very healthy at age seventy-five.（所有瓊斯先生的祖先都很健康長壽；同樣地，他在七十五歲時還很健康。）

He did not object to our proposal; *indeed*, he gave several reasons for supporting it.
（他不但不反對我們的提議，其實他還提出好幾個支持它的理由。）

The car was almost new; *again*, it was in excellent condition.
（這部車子幾乎是新的，而且狀況很好。）

【註】大體上 besides, moreover, furthermore 三字可以相互代用。

The engineer says that the plan is not practical; $\begin{cases} \textit{moreover,} \\ \textit{furthermore,} \\ \textit{besides,} \end{cases}$ he has other

objections.（工程師說那個計劃不實際，而且他還有其他的反對意見。）

但要在文法上仔細推敲，我們也可以找出下列的區別：

① **besides**：用來引導一個子句來加強前面的說明。

His project is an excellent one; *besides*, it is likely to help a great many people.
（他的計劃很好，而且它可能還可以幫助很多人。）

② **moreover**：比 besides 的語氣還要強些。

The mountain was steep and rugged; *moreover*, its sides were coated with ice.
（那座山既陡峭又崎嶇，而且山麓還被冰所覆蓋。）

③ **furthermore**：比前兩者的語氣都強，而且是最正式的用語，尤其在句中已用過
besides 或 moreover 時，要再強調時一定要用 furthermore，也可寫成 further。

He is well-liked; *moreover*, he is absolutely dependable; *furthermore*, there is
no one who can take his place.
（他廣受喜愛；而且他又是絕對可靠；最重要的是沒有人能取代他。）

8. **what is more**（**what's more**）（此外；而且）；**what is worse**（更糟的是）

I don't think the man is suitable for a gardener; he is lazy, stupid and unreliable, *what is
more*, he knows nothing about gardening.
（我不認爲那個人適合做園丁；他懶惰、愚蠢、不可靠，更甚者，他對園藝的事一竅不通。）

He learns easily, *and what is more*, he remembers what he has learnt.
（他容易學會，而且所學的全記得。）

I lost myself in the jungle, and *what was worse*, it was getting darker and darker.
（我在叢林中迷路了，更糟的是，天色越來越暗了。）

9. **never…but**（從來沒有…而不…；每次…就…）

It *never* rains *but* pours.（不雨則已，一雨傾盆。）

Ⅱ. **反義連接詞**（**Adversative Conjunctions**）：用來表示前後所說的意義恰好**相反或相互對
比**的連接詞，通常以 **"but"** 爲代表。

1. **but**：作「**但是**」解。連接兩個文法作用相同的單字、片語、子句或句子。

He is stupid *but* persevering.（他很愚蠢，但卻很堅忍不拔。）

Between men and women there is hatred, love, *but* no friendship.
（男女之間有恨、有愛，但絕沒有友誼。）

He may be a man of character, *but* cannot be a man of ability.
（他可能是個有個性的人，但不可能是個有能力的人。）

Fortune often knocks at the door, *but* the fool does not invite her in.
（幸運之神常來敲門，但呆子不會請她進來。）

Death is at all times terrible, *but* never so much so as at sea.
（死亡不論在什麼時候都很可怕，但絕不會比在海上死更可怕。）

【so much so = so terrible，so much so 的第二個 so 代替前面的 terrible，much 是加強程度的副詞
（詳見 p.537 註）】

Animals are guided by instinct, *but* man by reason.
（動物受本能支配，但人類卻受理性支配。）

【註】比較下列 **but** 的其他用法：

① but that（從屬連接詞）

I could easily do it *but that*（= were it not for the fact that）I have no time.
（我能輕而易舉地做它，但我沒時間。）

② but（介詞）除了…之外

but 用在前面有 no one, none, nothing 等否定詞、who 等疑問詞，或 all, everyone 等字時，*but* 是介詞，與 *except* 同義。（詳見 p.540, 564）

I have no friend *but* you.（除了你之外，我沒有朋友。）

③ but（準關係代名詞）（詳見 p.160）

There is no rule *but* has its exceptions.（凡是規則皆有例外。）

④ but（副詞）與 only 同義

She has *but* one aim in life, to be a movie star.

（她生活唯一的目標，就是想當個電影明星。）

2. $\left\{\begin{array}{l}\textbf{indeed}\cdots\textbf{but} \\ \textbf{It is true}\cdots\textbf{but} \\ \cdots\textbf{, to be sure, but}\end{array}\right\}$ 表示讓步後的強調語氣，作「**的確…不過**」解

Indeed he tried hard, *but* he did not succeed.（他的確很努力，但他並沒有成功。）

He has recovered *indeed*, *but* he is not as healthy as before.

（他的病的確是好了，但他卻不像以前那麼健康。）

It is true he is old, *but* he is still strong.（他的確是老了，不過他依然很強壯。）

= *To be sure* he is old, *but* he is still strong.

A good idea, *to be sure*, *but* it is hard to practice.（那的確個好主意，但難以實行。）

3. **一些表反義的副詞性連接詞**：只能用來連接兩個子句。

(1) $\left\{\begin{array}{l}\textbf{whereas} \\ \textbf{while}\end{array}\right\}$（= **but on the contrary**）（相反地；然而）

Wise men love truth, *whereas* fools shun it.（聰明人愛真理，而傻子卻逃避它。）

Some people like fat meat, *whereas* others hate it.（有些人喜歡肥肉，而有些人討厭肥肉。）

He went out, *while* I stayed at home.（他出去了，而我則留在家裡。）

(2) **only**（但是；只是）：與 but 同義，常用於口語中。only 之前可用分號或逗點。

He promises, *only* he does not keep his word.（他答應了，但卻沒有遵守諾言。）

Go wherever you like; *only* do not stay here.（你愛去哪裡就去哪裡，就是不要待在這裡。）

You may go, *only* return quickly.（你可以去，不過要快點回來。）

Come when you please, *only* let me know when I may expect you.

（高興的時候就來，但須讓我知道什麼時候可以等你來。）

(3) **still**（但是；然而）：still 前面用逗點或分號均可。

The weather is very hot, *still* it is not unbearable.（天氣是很熱，但還不是令人無法忍受。）

He failed again, *still* he did not lose hope.（他又失敗了，但是他並不灰心。）

I am tired; *still* I will walk further.（我累是累了，但是我還要再走遠一點。）

(4) **yet, and yet, but yet**（但是）：與 but 同義。

He is very rich, *yet* he is not contented.（他很有錢，但他並不滿足。）

He is always polite to me, *and yet* I don't like him.

（他對我總是很有禮貌，但我並不喜歡他。）

In this life, we can not be entirely blessed, ***but yet*** we may be completely miserable.
（在今生今世，我們不可能全然幸福，但卻可能完全不幸。）

⑸ **however**（然而；但是）：however 前面通常用分號，可放在句首、句中、句尾。

Our task is hard; ***however***, we should persevere to the end.
（我們的工作是困難的，但我們應該堅持到底。）

I shall not oppose your design; I cannot, ***however***, approve of it.
（我不會反對你的設計，但我也不可能贊成它。）

⑹ **nevertheless**（然而；但是）

He has faults; ***nevertheless***, we love him.（他有缺點，可是我們還是愛他。）

He finds life difficult; ***nevertheless*** he does not give up hope.
（他覺得生活很困難，然而他並未放棄希望。）

All men were against him; ***nevertheless***, he persevered.
（所有人都反對他，可是他卻堅持到底。）

【註】 上面所提之反義副詞性連接詞均有相同的意義，到底要怎樣區別它們呢？可分成下列兩點
說明：

1. 大體上 **still**, **yet**, **however**, **nevertheless** 可相互換用。

On the way to the station, we were delayed by heavy traffic; $\left\{\begin{array}{l} \textit{yet,} \\ \textit{still,} \\ \textit{however,} \\ \textit{nevertheless,} \end{array}\right.$

we managed to catch the train.
（在去車站的途中，我們被繁忙的交通所耽擱；但是我們還是設法趕上那班火車。）

2. 如果要按文法仔細地推敲則：

① **but**：只是表前後敘述相反，但沒有強調之意。

This is not winter, ***but*** it is almost as cold.（現在不是冬天，但幾乎像冬天一樣冷。）

② **however**：表相反，但是語氣較弱，因此常用於**插入句**。

This is not winter; it is, ***however***, almost as cold.
（現在雖然不是冬天，可是幾乎像冬天一樣冷。）

however 也可做句子的轉承語，表「**最後的結論**」或「**最後的決定**」。

He will probably fail in the examination. ***However***, I am quite willing to let him
try it.（他大概會考不及格，但是我很願意讓他試一試。）

③ **still** 和 **nevertheless**, **yet** 相似，用來**說明一強烈相反（對比）的結論**，不過 still 與
yet 的語氣較強。

It is true that winter is over; ***still***, it is almost as cold.
（的確多天已過去，可是天氣還是一樣的冷。）

To be sure, it is no longer winter; ***nevertheless***, it is quite cold.
（的確，多天已過去了，可是天氣卻十分寒冷。）

Say what you will; we must, ***nevertheless***, go forward.
（不論你說什麼，而我們都必須努力向前。）

It is well on in May, *yet* it is almost as cold as midwinter.

（雖然已是五月天，可是天氣幾乎像隆冬一樣冷。）

Although I have known him only a few years, *yet* he is my best friend.

（雖然我認識他只有幾年，但他是我最好的朋友。）（參照 p.526）

(7) $\left\{ \begin{array}{l} \textbf{on the other hand} \\ \textbf{on the contrary} \end{array} \right\}$ （另一方面；相反地）

Father and mother wanted to go for a ride; the children, *on the other hand*, wanted to stay home and play with their friends.【副詞性連接詞可放在子句的句首、句中或句末】

（父母親要開車去兜風；但另一方面，孩子要待在家裡和朋友們玩。）

Games are very good for one; *on the other hand*, one must not play too much.

（遊戲對人很有好處；但在另一方面，人們不能玩得太多。）

The principal thought that the children went to the zoo; *on the contrary*, they went to the bakery.（校長以為孩子們去了動物園；相反地，他們去了麵包店。）

He is not a stupid boy; *on the contrary*, he is quite intelligent.

（他不是個傻孩子；相反地，他很聰明。）

III. 選擇連接詞（Alternative Conjunctions）：是將兩個部分連在一起，而在其中選擇一個，其代表字為 "**or**"。

1. or

⑴ 作「**或**」解

You *or* your sister has to go.（你或你妹妹必須去。）

Is he guilty *or* innocent?（他是有罪或無罪？）

Are you going to the party, *or* will you stay home?

（你是要去舞會，或是要留在家裡？）

【註】or 連接兩主詞時，其動詞與最接近的主詞一致。

$\left\{ \begin{array}{l} \text{You } \textit{or} \text{ he } \textit{have} \text{ taken away my umbrella. 【誤】} \\ \text{You } \textit{or} \text{ he } \textbf{\textit{has}} \text{ taken away my umbrella. 【正】} \\ \text{（是你或是他把我的雨傘拿走了。）} \end{array} \right.$

$\left\{ \begin{array}{l} \text{You } \textit{or} \text{ I } \textit{are} \text{ mistaken. 【誤】} \\ \text{You } \textit{or} \text{ I } \textbf{\textit{am}} \text{ mistaken. 【正】} \\ \text{（你錯了，或者是我錯了。）} \end{array} \right.$

⑵ 作「**大約**」解

It costs a hundred dollars *or* so.（它值大約一百元。）

The price is one dollar *or* thirty-two N.T.（價格是一美元，即三十二元台幣。）

⑶ 作「**否則**」解

He must return the book today, *or* he will have to pay a fine.

（他今天就必須還書，否則他必須付罰金。）

Hurry up, *or* you will be late for school.（趕快，否則你上學要遲到了。）

= If you do not hurry up, you will be late for school.

⑷ **相對意思之結合，表讓步**

Rain *or* shine, I'll go. (不論晴雨，我都會去。)

Money *or* no money, he made up his mind to carry out his plan.

（不論有沒有錢，他都下定決心要實行他的計劃。）

2. **not…but**（不…而）

What he lacks is *not* intelligence *but* perseverance.（他缺乏的不是智慧，而是毅力。）

His wife did *not* scold him, *but* comforted him instead.（他太太沒有責罵他，反而安慰他。）

Not money *but* wisdom is what we want.（我們所需要的不是金錢，而是智慧。）

Many people talk, *not* because they have anything to say, *but* for the mere love of talking.

（很多人說話，並不是因為有話要說，而只是因為愛說話而已。）

A man's value should *not* be estimated by his position in society *but* by his character.

（一個人的價值不應該以其社會地位來衡量，而應以其品格來衡量。）

3. **either…or**（不是…就是）：用來連接對等的單字、片語或子句，如果連接兩個主詞時，動詞和第二個主詞一致。

You must come *either* on Monday *or* on Tuesday; I am too busy to see you any other day.

（你必須在週一或週二來；其他的日子我太忙不能見你。）

You must be *either* for *or* against the idea.〔你（必須）不是贊成就是反對這個想法。〕

There is no standing still in this life; one must *either* advance *or* fall behind.

（在這人生中不可能靜止不動；不前進就是落後了。）

Either he *or* I *am* to blame.（不是他就是我該受責備。）

4. **一些表選擇的副詞性連接詞：**

else
or (**else**)　⎱（否則）：用來連接兩個對等子句。else 和 or (else) 之前可用分號或逗點。
otherwise⎰

You must study hard; *else* you will fail.（你一定要努力用功，不然你會失敗。）

He has some real sorrow, *else* he would not weep so much.

（他一定真有傷心事，不然他不會哭得如此厲害。）

Do your work, *or else* you will be punished.（做你的工作，否則你會被罰。）

The leaders settled the argument; *otherwise*, there would have been war.

（領袖們解決了爭論，不然將會有戰爭。）

Leave the room; *otherwise* you will be caught.（離開這房間，否則你會被抓住。）

Ⅳ. **推理連接詞（Illative Conjunctions）**：此類連接詞都是連接兩個子句，所以**全部為副詞性連接詞**，以 "**so**" 為代表。

1. (**and**) **so**（所以；因此）

It is now late, *so* we had better go to bed.（現在時間很晚了，所以我們最好上床睡覺。）

He was very tired from walking, *and so* he sat down to take a little rest.

（他走路走得很疲倦，所以他坐下來休息一下。）

He was born and brought up in America, (*and*) *so* he can speak English.

（他生長在美國，所以會說英語。）

2. **(and) therefore**（因此；所以）

You have disobeyed me; *therefore*, I will not help you again.
（你曾經違背過我，所以我不會再幫助你了。）

He was in bad health, *and therefore* he could not go to school.
（他不健康，所以無法去上學。）

He has done very good work for the society; *therefore*, he deserves great praise.
（他為這個社會做了很好的事，所以他應該大受讚揚。）

3. **thus**（因此；於是）

He studied hard; *thus* he got high marks.（他用功讀書，因此獲得高分。）

Industries thrive where coal abounds; *thus* you will find coal mines and many factories
　　side by side.（煤產豐富的地方工業都很發達，因此你可以看到煤礦和許多工廠並立著。）

4. **(and) consequently**（因此；所以）

The road was wet and slippery; *consequently*, there were many accidents.
（道路又濕又滑，所以很多意外事故。）

Singapore lies very near to the equator; *consequently*, the weather is very hot all the year
　　round.（新加坡位於赤道附近，所以天氣一年到頭都很熱。）

I overslept, *and consequently* I was late.（我睡過頭了，所以遲到了。）

5. **(and) accordingly**（因此；所以）

He requested an opportunity to make up for his absences; *accordingly*, his teacher gave
　　him special help.（他請求一個彌補他缺席的機會，所以他老師給他特別的幫助。）

There is no demand in Taipei for this make of car; *accordingly*, I am not able to give
　　you any orders.（台北沒有此種廠牌車的需求，所以我不能給你任何訂單。）

He was not at home, *and accordingly* I left my card.（他不在家，所以我留下了名片。）

6. **then**; **so then**（然後；那麼）

I will study medicine for seven years; *then* I will be a doctor.
（我將研讀七年的醫學，然後我會成為一位醫師。）

You have been there; *so then*, you must have seen him.
（你曾到過那裡，那麼，你一定見過他了。）

【註】 **and then**（然後；而且）【then 是副詞】

We had a week in Rome *and then* went to Naples.
（我們在羅馬住了一個星期，然後前往那不勒斯。）【and then = and after that】

The dress seems too good to throw away, *and then* it is very becoming.
（這件衣服似乎很好不應丟掉，而且很合適。）【and then = and also】

7. **hence**（因此；所以）【hence 之前可用逗點或分號】

You must meet the deadline; *hence*, a decision is needed now.
（你必須趕上截止期限，所以現在就需要做個決定。）

It is very late, *hence* you must go to bed.
（時間很晚了，所以你必須上床睡覺。）

【註】上面所說的那些推理的副詞性連接詞，其中文意思大都為「**因此；所以**」，大體上可以相互代替使用：

Our plane was five hours late; $\left\{\begin{array}{l}\textit{therefore,}\\ \textit{consequently,}\\ \textit{thus,}\end{array}\right\}$ we did not arrive in time for the

conference.（我們的飛機遲了五小時，因此我們沒能及時趕上開會。）

但要在文法上**仔細推敲**，我們也可在其中找出一些差異來：

① **therefore, hence** 作「**因此**」解，是最正式的用語，用在數學、理則學或其他精細的議論中，表嚴格的推理；後面的結論是前面前提的必然結果。

All men are rational beings. John Jones is a man; *therefore*, John Jones is a rational being.（所有人都是理性動物，約翰瓊斯是人，所以他是個理性動物。）

hence 與 **therefore** 在很多情形下是可以互換使用的；不過 **hence** 更強調前面的前提。

Both statements may be false, but both cannot be true since they are contradictory; *hence*, if A be true, B is false, or if B be true, A is false.
（兩個說法都可能是假的，但兩者絕不可能都是真的，因為它們是相互矛盾；因此，如果說 A 是真，B 一定是假，或者 B 是真，則 A 是假。）

② **consequently** 作「**因此；結果**」解，特指**因果關係**。

He was injured in an accident; *consequently*, he has not been at his office in months.（他在一場意外中受傷了，因此他幾個月都沒有去辦公室了。）

③ **then** 被用來指示**邏輯的順序**，特別強調結果，常用於條件句，即 "If…, then…" 的句型中。

If A is true, *then* B is false.（假如 A 是真的，那麼 B 就是假。）

④ **accordingly** 是**表自然的結果**，不像 consequently 表必然的結果。

He said he was hungry; *accordingly*, they shared their meager lunch with him.
（他說他餓了，所以他們和他分食他們不足的午飯。）

⑤ **so** 用於通俗的日常會話中，但應避免使用得太多。

The day was fine *and so* we set out.（天氣很好，所以我們就出發了。）

V. 解釋連接詞（Explanatory Conjunctions）：用來解釋的連接詞，表**原因**或**舉例**等，以 "**for**" 為代表。

1. for（因為）

He must have passed this way, *for* here are his footprints.
（他一定是走這條路，因為這裡有他的腳印。）

It must have rained during the night, *for* the road is wet.
（夜裡一定下雨了，因為路上是濕的。）

【註 1】 **for 與 so 的比較**：

當 for 連接兩個子句時，第一個子句表結果或結論，第二個子句是說明產生前述結果的原因。但 so 要是連接兩個子句時，正好與 for 所連接的子句相反，第一個子句是敘述原因，第二個子句則說明由前述原因所產生的結果。

He is very popular with students, *for* he is a good teacher.
（他很受學生歡迎，因爲他是個好老師。）
He is a good teacher, *so* he is very popular with students.
（他是位好老師，所以他很受學生歡迎。）

I never try to give anybody advice, *for* I know nothing is more unwelcome than advice.
（我從來不想給任何人勸告，因爲我知道沒有事情比勸告更不受歡迎。）
I know nothing is more unwelcome than advice, *so* I never try to give it to anybody.（我知道沒有事情比勸告更不受歡迎，所以我從不想給任何人勸告。）

【註 2】 **because 與 for 的比較**：

① **because 爲從屬連接詞**，引導副詞子句；**for 爲對等連接詞**，連接兩個對等子句，爲了與介詞 for 區分，通常在其前加**逗點**（,）。

② **because 所引導的子句可放在句首**；**for 的子句不能放在句首**，應置於表結果的子句後面。

For he was a brave man, he felt no fear.【誤】
He felt no fear, *for* he was a brave man.【正】
（他不害怕，因爲他是個勇者。）

③ **because 所表示的是原因**，是**直接的理由**；**for 所表示的是附加的理由**，是推斷的理由。

The light went out, *because* the oil was out.【表原因】
The oil must be out, *for* the light went out.【表推斷的理由】

He is loved by all, *because* he is honest.【表直接的理由】
He must be honest, *for* he is loved by all.【表推斷的理由】

It will probably rain *because* there is a dark cloud approaching.【表原因】
It will rain, *for* the barometer is falling.【表推斷的理由】

我們絕不能說 *It will rain, because the barometer is falling.* 因爲 barometer（氣壓表）的下降，不是下雨的原因。我們反而可以說：The barometer is falling because it is going to rain. 因爲「快要下雨了」倒是造成氣壓表下降的原因。總之，是「下雨造成氣壓表下降，不是氣壓表下降造成下雨」，我們豈可本末倒置！

④ **because 可用於回答**；**for 不可以用來回答問題**。

Why did you beat him?（你爲什麼打他？）
I beat him { *for*【誤】 / *because*【正】 } I was angry.（我打他是因爲我生氣了。）

⑤ **for** 不能用於 **not…but** 的句型中。

He stole not $\begin{Bmatrix} \textit{for}【誤】 \\ \textit{because}【正】 \end{Bmatrix}$ he wanted the money, but $\begin{Bmatrix} \textit{for}【誤】 \\ \textit{because}【正】 \end{Bmatrix}$ he liked stealing.（他不是因為需要錢而偷，而是因為喜歡偷。）

⑥ 在 "**It is because…that**" 的句型中，不可將 **because** 換成 **for**。

It was $\begin{Bmatrix} \textit{for}【誤】 \\ \textit{because}【正】 \end{Bmatrix}$ he was ill that he could not come.

（因為他生病了，所以不能來。）

⑦ **because** 所引導的子句可以當 **be** 動詞的補語，而 **for** 所引導的子句不可當 be 動詞的補語。

It is $\begin{Bmatrix} \textit{for}【誤】 \\ \textit{because}【正】 \end{Bmatrix}$ he is lazy.（那是因為他懶惰。）

⑧ **because** 可以由副詞修飾，而 **for** 不可。

She lost her position <u>simply</u> $\begin{Bmatrix} \textit{for}【誤】 \\ \textit{because}【正】 \end{Bmatrix}$ she refused to tell a lie.

（她失去了她的職位，只因為她拒絕說謊。）

2. such as

I require some books of reference, *such as* a dictionary, a gazetteer, etc.
（我需要一些參考書，像是一本字典，一本地名辭典等。）

3. 其他一些表解釋的副詞性連接詞：

namely（= viz. 即；也就是）；*that is* *(to say)*（= i.e. = id est. 換言之；也就是）；*for example*（= e.g. = exempli gratia 例如）；*for instance*（例如）；*(let us) say*（例如）；*to wit*（即；也就是）。上述除了 (let us) say 之前通常用逗點之外，其他副詞性連接詞之前可用逗點或分號。

Three boys were absent; *namely*, Tom, Dick, and Harry.
（三個男生缺席，他們是湯姆、迪克和哈利。）

Susan is a good student; *that is* (to say), she gets good grades in school.
（蘇珊是個好學生，也就是說，她在學校得到高的分數。）

Many great men have risen from poverty — Lincoln and Edison, *for example*.
（許多偉人由貧困中崛起，例如林肯和愛迪生。）

There are jobs more dangerous than truck driving; *for instance*, training lions.
（有些工作比開卡車還要危險，例如訓練獅子。）

There are plenty of things to keep you busy, *say*, hiking and fishing.
（有很多事情可以讓你很忙，例如健行和釣魚。）
【*(let us) say* 也可視為插入語，是句子的獨立成份，參閱 p.650】

She left me all her land in her will, *to wit*, the three farms.
（她遺囑交代將她所有的土地，即那三個農場留給我。）

第三章　從屬連接詞（**Subordinate Conjunctions**）

連接從屬子句和主要子句的連接詞稱爲從屬連接詞，按其作用又可分爲：引導名詞子句的從屬連接詞、引導形容詞子句的從屬連接詞，和引導副詞子句的從屬連接詞等三種。

I. 引導名詞子句的從屬連接詞

1. **that**（that 除了引導名詞子句，還可引導副詞子句表目的或結果，引導形容詞子句時 that 本身是關係代名詞，現僅敘述 that 引導名詞子句的用法。）

   ***That** he loved her* was certain.【that 引導名詞子句做 was 的主詞】

   = It was certain ***that** he loved her.*【that 引導名詞子句做真正主詞，It 是形式主詞】
   （他愛她是確實的。）

   They say (***that***) *he is a great scientist.*【that 引導名詞子句做 say 的受詞】
   （聽說他是個偉大的科學家。）

   I think it certain ***that** he will succeed.*【that 引導名詞子句做 think 的真正受詞，it 是形式受詞】
   （我認爲他一定會成功。）

   The problem is ***that** we have not much money.*【that 引導名詞子句做主詞補語】
   （問題在於我們沒有多少錢。）

   The thought ***that** he will help me* gives me courage.【that 引導名詞子句做 thought 的同位語】
   （他會幫助我的這種想法，給了我勇氣。）

   【註 1】 **that** 的省略與保留

   ① **that** 子句做主詞時，**that** 不可省略。

   > *She was here* can be proved.【誤】
   > ***That** she was here* can be proved.【正】
   > （她曾在此可以被證實。）

   ② **that** 子句做受詞時，時常省略。

   I don't think (***that***) *he will come.*（我想他不會來。）
   I wish (***that***) *there would be no more misunderstanding between us.*
   （我希望我們之間不會再有誤會存在。）

   但在 **suggest, order** 等動詞之後 **that** 原則上不可省略。（參閱 p.372）
   I *suggest **that*** we should go to the theater.（我建議去看戲。）

   在 **S + V + it + 受詞補語 + that** 子句的句型中，**that** 不可省略。

   > We all considered it a pity *you could not come with us.*【誤】
   > We all considered it a pity ***that** you could not come with us.*【正】
   > （你不能跟我們來，我們都覺得好可惜。）

③ 由對等連接詞 **and** 或 **but** 所連接的兩個做受詞的 that 子句中，**第一個子句的 that 可以省略，但第二個不可省略。**

He said (***that***) *he had eaten nothing* but ***that*** *he was not hungry.*
　　　　　可省略　　　　　　　　　　　　　　　不可省略

（他說他沒有吃東西，但是他不餓。）

④ **在 sorry, glad, aware, surprised, delighted, disappointed…後的 that 可省略，**此 that 子句應該是名詞子句，因為 that 子句不可直接做介詞的受詞，而將介詞省略（詳閱註5）。也有少數文法家視此 that 子句為副詞子句，是 because 的代用字。

I am sure (***that***) you are honest. （我確定你是誠實的。）

= I am sure of your being honest.

I am sorry (***that***) you fell out of love. （很遺憾你失戀了。）

We were delighted (***that***) business was on the upgrade.

（我們很高興生意興隆。）

【註2】 **為避免重複，在有些動詞之後肯定的 that 子句常用 so 代替，否定的 that 子句常用 not 代替。**（詳閱 p.128 so 的用法）

　　　┌ A: Will he come? （他會來嗎？）
　　　└ B: I think *so*. (= I think *he will come*.)（我想他會來。）

　　　┌ A: It's going to rain. （要下雨了。）
　　　└ B: I hope *not*. (= I hope *it will not rain*.)（我希望不要下雨。）

【註3】 **作受詞用的 that 子句後不可接受詞補語，**一定要用 it 代替 that 子句，並將 that 子句放在補語後面。

　　　┌ I think *that he will succeed certain*. 【誤】
　　　│
　　　└ I think ***it*** certain ***that*** *he will succeed*. （我認為他一定會成功。）【正】
　　　　　　　　　　受詞補語

【註4】 **that 子句不能做介詞的受詞，**但有少數例外，如 but, except, save, in, notwithstanding 等，可直接用 that 子句當受詞，**但和 that 結合成特殊的意義。**

He would have helped us ***but that*** he was short of money at that time.
（如果不是因為他那時候沒有錢，他會幫助我們的。）【**but that　如果不是因為**】

This is all right ***except that*** we don't have any entertainment.
（除了我們沒有任何娛樂外，一切都還好。）【**except that　除了…之外**】

We know nothing about him ***save that*** he was in the army during the war.
（除了知道他戰爭時曾在陸軍服務以外，我們對他一無所知。）【**save that = except that**】

The higher income tax is harmful ***in that*** it may discourage people from trying to earn more. 【**in that = because**】
（所得稅提高是有害的，因為它可能使人們不想多賺錢。）

He went ***notwithstanding that*** he was ordered not to.
（雖然被命令不許去，他還是去了。）【**notwithstanding that　雖然**】

【註5】 that 子句除了前面所舉的幾個介詞外，不能作爲其他介詞的受詞，故**須將介詞省略後才可接 that 子句**。若介詞不省略，則須加 it，或加 **the fact** 或依句意採用其他名詞爲媒介，使 **that 子句**做 **it** 或 **the fact** 等的同位語；it 和 the fact 本身沒有意義，純粹爲了滿足文法上的需要。當然也可把名詞子句改成（動）名詞，即「介詞＋動名詞」的形式。

You may depend on *it that every member of the committee will support your proposal.*
（你放心好了，委員會的每一位委員都會支持你的提議。）【that 子句是 it 的同位語】

How can you account for *the fact that the airplane can fly*?
（你要如何說明飛機能飛的原因呢？）【that 子句做 the fact 的同位語】

I'll personally see *that your daughter receives the best medical care there is.*
【介詞 to 省略】

= I'll personally see to *it that your daughter receives the best medical care there is.*
【that 子句是 it 的同位語】

（我會親自注意讓你的女兒獲得現有最好的醫療。）

The farmer boasts *that he owns a thousand acres of good land.* 【介詞 of 省略】
= The farmer boasts *of owning a thousand acres of good land.* 【介詞＋動名詞】
（那農夫吹噓自己擁有一千畝良田。）

I agreed (with *the opinion*) *that the meeting should be postponed.*
（我同意會議延期。）【that 子句做 the opinion 的同位語】

【註6】 **做同位語的 that 子句和 that 所引導的形容詞子句的區別**：引導名詞子句的 that 是純粹的連接詞；而引導形容詞子句的 that 是關係代名詞，它在形容詞子句中必有代名作用，做主詞、受詞或補語。

名詞子句做同位語
The fact *that* he is a good teacher is well known. 【that 是連接詞】
連接詞
（他是個好老師是眾所周知的。）

形容詞子句
The news *that* he told me yesterday is not true.
關代
（他昨天告訴我的消息是不實的。）【that 是關係代名詞，在子句中做 told 的直接受詞】

【註7】 在表示詢問及懷疑之類的動詞，如 **ask**（問），**doubt**（懷疑）等之後，**不可接 that 子句爲受詞**。但 doubt 作「不信」解，表示強烈的不相信時，可接 that 子句。（參照 p.485）

Please ask (her) *that she will be back.* 【誤】
Please ask (her) *when she will be back.* 【正】〔請問問（她）她將於何時回來。〕

I doubt *that he will come.* 【正】（我不相信他會來。）
= I don't think that he will come.
I doubt *whether he will come.* 【正】（我懷疑他是否會來。）

當然 do not doubt（＝ believe）**和疑問句中的 doubt 可接 that 子句做受詞。**

I *do not doubt* that he will come.（我相信他會來。）

Do you *doubt* that he will succeed?（你懷疑他不會成功嗎？）

【註 8】　**that** 子句不可做下列動詞的受詞：

admire（稱讚）	allow（允許）	behold（看到）	bid（命令）
cause（引起）	celebrate（慶祝）	condemn（註定）	dislike（厭惡）
entreat（懇求）	force（強迫）	hate（厭惡）	hear（聽見）
help（幫助）	let（讓）	like（喜歡）	loathe（嫌惡）
love（愛）	overlook（忽視）	refuse（拒絕）	see（看）
take（認為）	want（想要）		

I admire *that you are never late.*【誤】
I admire your never being late.【正】
（我欽佩你從來不遲到。）

Let us celebrate *that we were successful.*【誤】
Let us celebrate our success.【正】
（讓我們為成功而慶祝。）

She does not like *that her boy play rugby.*【誤】
She does not like her boy to play rugby.【正】
（她不喜歡她兒子打橄欖球。）

I overlooked *that he had made some serious mistakes.*【誤】
I overlooked the fact that he had made some serious mistakes.【正】
（我沒有注意到他犯了一些嚴重的錯誤。）

The school refused *that he should go.*【誤】
The school refused to let him go.【正】
（學校拒絕讓他去。）

I take *that we are to come early.*【誤】
I take it that we are to come early.【正】
（我以為我們該早來。）

I want *that he should go at once.*
【誤，但在美國英語中 want 後可接 that 子句，本句僅在美國可用】
I want him to go at once.（我要他立刻去。）【正】

【注意】　**see** 當「覺得」或「發現」解時，**hear** 當「聽說」解時，可接 **that** 子句做受詞。

I saw（= felt）***that he would not help us***.
（我覺得他不會幫助我們。）

I saw（= found）***that nobody was in the room***.
（我發現房間裡沒有人。）

Have you heard ***that Smith is sick***?
（你聽說史密斯生病了嗎？）

【註9】　**that** 子句不可做下列動詞的直接受詞：

accuse（控告）	advise（勸告）	blame（責備）	congratulate（祝賀）
denounce（譴責）	envy（羨慕；嫉妒）	excuse（原諒）	forgive（原諒）
impress（使有印象）	order（命令）	refuse（拒絕）	

He accused me *that I copied.*【誤】
He accused me of copying.【正】
（他控告我抄襲。）

Don't blame me *that I did not write to you.*【誤】
Don't blame me for not writing to you.【正】
（不要責怪我沒有寫信給你。）

I congratulate you *that you have graduated.*【誤】
I congratulate you upon your graduation.【正】
（恭喜你畢業。）

They denounce us *that we are imperialistic.*【誤】
They denounce us for being imperialistic.【正】
（他們譴責我們為帝國主義。）

We envied him *that he learned so easily.*【誤】
We envied him the ease with which he learned.【正】
We envied his learning so easily.【正】
（我們羨慕他很容易就學會。）

Excuse me *that I interrupt you.*【誤】
Excuse me for interrupting you.【正】
Excuse my interrupting you.【正】
（原諒我打擾了你。）

He would not forgive *that we slighted him.*【誤】
He would not forgive us for slighting him.【正】
He would not forgive our slighting him.【正】
（他不會原諒我們藐視他。）

He impressed the teacher *that he had done good work.*【誤】
He impressed the teacher with the good work he had done.【正】
（他的工作做得很好，讓老師印象深刻。）

Please forgive me *that I broke my promise.*【誤】
Please forgive me for breaking my promise.【正】
Please forgive my breaking my promise.【正】
（請原諒我沒有遵守諾言。）

2. whether; whether…or (not)

Whether *he will come* is doubtful.【whether 引導名詞子句做 is 的主詞】

= It is doubtful ***whether*** *he will come*.【whether 引導名詞子句做 is 的真正主詞，It 是形式主詞】

（他是否會來還不知道。）

I asked him ***whether*** *he would go out* (***or not***).

（我問他是否會出去。）【whether 引導名詞子句做 asked 的直接受詞】

Everything depends upon ***whether*** *we have enough money*.

（一切都要看我們是否有足夠的錢。）【whether 引導名詞子句做介系詞 upon 的受詞】

The question is ***whether*** *he should go at once*.【whether 引導名詞子句做主詞補語】

（問題在他該不該馬上走。）

The question ***whether*** *we ought to call in a specialist* will be answered by the family doctor.

（我們該不該請個專科醫生這個問題將由家庭醫生來決定。）

【whether 引導名詞子句做 question 的同位語】

【**註 1**】 下面四句的意思相同。**whether…or not** 的 **not** 可以代替一個否定的子句，或寫成 **whether or not…**。

> I do not know ***whether*** *he is well* ***or not***.
> I do not know ***whether*** *he is well* ***or*** *whether he is* ***not*** *well*.【較不常用】
> I do not know ***whether or not*** *he is well*.
> I do not know ***whether*** *he is well* ***or is*** ***not*** *well*.【較不常用】
> （我不知道他身體是否安好。）

＊ **whether or no** 是副詞片語，作「無論如何；必定」解。

I'll go ***whether or no***.（我無論如何一定要走。）

【**註 2**】 下面三句的意思略有不同：

I do not know ***whether*** *he is well* ***or not***.（我不知道他的身體是否安好。）

I do not know ***whether*** *he is well*.

（我不知道他的身體可好。—— 我懷疑他的身體不好。）

I do not know ***whether*** *he is* ***not*** *well*.

（我不知道他的身體是否不好。—— 我想他的身體並非不好。）

【**註 3**】 whether…or 所引導的子句，有時是表讓步的副詞子句，但 or…不可省略。

I'll start next week, ***whether*** *it rains* ***or not***.

（不管下星期有沒有下雨，我都會出發。）

Whether *you go* ***or*** *stay*, I am going.（不管你去不去，我是要去的。）

Whether *he is young* ***or*** *old*, I don't care at all.

（不管他是年輕或是年老，我一點也不在乎。）

【註 4】　**whether** 和 **that** 的比較：（參照 p.481）

> I doubt *that* he is guilty.（我不信他有罪。）【doubt 作「不信」解時，可接 that 子句】
> = I don't think that he is guilty.

> I suspect *that* he is guilty.（我懷疑他有罪。）
> = I think that he is guilty.

> I doubt *whether*（= *if*）he is guilty.（我不知道他是否有罪。）
> = I am not sure if he is guilty.

3. **if**

if 引導名詞子句接在 **ask, see, try, wonder, doubt, know** 等字之後，或在含有「詢問」或「懷疑」之類的句子中，等於 **whether**。

名詞子句做真正主詞

It is doubtful *if*（= *whether*）he will come.（他會不會來尚未確定。）

I wonder *if*（= *whether*）it will rain tomorrow.

（我不知道明天會不會下雨。）【if 引導名詞子句做 wonder 的受詞】

I asked him *if*（= *whether*）he would go with me.

（我問他是不是要和我一起去。）【if 引導名詞子句做 asked 的直接受詞】

【註 1】　**if** 與 **whether** 常通用，但 **whether** 子句做主詞且置於句首時，不可以 **if** 代之。

> *Whether* we need it is a different matter.【正】
> （我們是否需要它是另一回事。）
> *If* we need it is a different matter.【誤】

【註 2】　**whether** 與 **if** 子句做動詞的受詞時，**if** 與 **whether** 通用，但句子中有 **or not** 時不得用 **if**。如做介系詞受詞只可用 **whether**。

I don't know *whether* (*or if*) we need it.（我不知道我們是否需要它。）
It does not matter *whether* she will come *or not*.（她來不來都沒關係。）
He was worried about *whether* he passed the French examination.
（他擔心是否通過了法文考試。）

【註 3】　**whether** 子句做補語時，不可用 **if** 代之。

> The question is *whether* we need it.（問題是我們是否需要它。）【正】
> The question is *if we need it.*【誤】

【註 4】　**whether** + 不定詞時，也不可用 **if** 代之。

> I don't know *whether to go or not.*（我不知道是否要去。）【正】
> I don't know *if to go or not.*【誤】

【註 5】　若 **if** 在句子中容易被誤解為「假如」而引導一個副詞子句時，應用 **whether** 而避免用 **if**。

名詞子句

Let me know *whether you are coming.*（告訴我你是否要來。）

副詞子句

Let me know *if you are coming.*（如果你要來，要讓我知道。）

4. **lest**

lest 用於 **fear, be afraid, danger, terror, tremble** 等表恐懼或危險的字後面等於 **that**，
lest 引導的子句常與 **should** 連用，**should** 也可省略。

名 詞 子 句

> We fear *lest he (**should**) take her life.*（我們害怕他會殺死她。）
> = We fear *that he **would** take her life.*

> We are afraid *lest he (**should**) get here too late.*【lest 引導名詞子句做 are afraid 的受詞】
> = We are afraid *that he **will** get here too late.*
> （我們怕他會太晚到這裡。）

There was danger *lest the plan (**should**) be known.*【lest 引導名詞子句做 danger 的同位語】
（恐怕這計劃有洩露的危險。）

He is terrorized *lest someone discover that his uncle was a horse thief.*
（他害怕有人發覺他叔叔是個馬賊。）

I tremble *lest he be discovered.*（我害怕他會被發現。）【should 省略】

She was wondering *lest the heir should be in any danger.*
（她懷疑這繼承人處在危險之中。）

【註】lest 還可引導表否定目的的副詞子句。(詳見 p.514)

He ran away *lest he **should** be seen.*（他為了怕被人看見而逃跑了。）

5.
> **but**
> **but that**
> **but what**

⑴ 用在疑問詞或否定字之後，等於 "that…not"。

名 詞 子 句 做 受 詞

> Who knows *but that the king may be here*?（誰曉得國王不會來到這裡？）
> = Who knows *that the king may **not** be here*?

I could hardly believe *but that it was true.*（我幾乎不能相信那不是真的。）

⑵ 用在 no doubt, not deny…等字之後，等於 "that"。

名 詞 子 句 做 同 位 語

There can be no doubt *but that she was lovely.*（她很可愛是無庸置疑的。）

I do not deny *but that I know him.*（我不否認我認識他。）

He did not doubt *but the prince would be moved to pardon him.*
（他不懷疑王子會受感動而原諒他。）

I could not deny *but what this was a very clever management.*
（我不能否認這是很聰明的手段。）

【註】本組連接詞還可引導表結果的副詞子句。(詳見 p.519)

6. **疑問代名詞：who, whom, whose, what, which** 除了引導名詞子句外，**在其所引導的子句裡必有代名作用，做主詞、受詞或補語**。(詳見 p.144)

名詞子句

I don't know ***who she is***. (我不知道她是誰。)

【who 引導名詞子句做 know 的受詞，在該子句中 who 做主詞補語】

名詞子句

We are wondering to ***whom this hat belongs***. (我們不知道這頂帽子是誰的。)

【whom 引導名詞子句做 wondering 的受詞，在該子句中 whom 做 belongs to 的受詞，所以用受格】

名詞子句

Tell me ***whose it was***. (告訴我這是誰的。)

【whose 引導名詞子句做 tell 的受詞，在該子句中 whose 做主詞補語】

名詞子句

I asked her ***what was the matter with her***. (我問她她怎麼了。)
　　　　　　主詞

【what 引導名詞子句做 asked 的受詞，在該子句中 what 做 was 的主詞】

名詞子句

She asked me ***which I liked best***. (她問我最喜歡哪一個。)

【which 引導名詞子句做 asked 的受詞，在該子句中 which 做 liked 的受詞】

【註】 **whose, which, what** 也可當作疑問形容詞，在其所引導的子句裡有形容詞作用，疑問形容詞加上所修飾的字，用法便和疑問代名詞相同，也可引導名詞子句。(參照 p.166)

Do you know ***whose hat it is***? (你知不知道那是誰的帽子？)

【whose 引導名詞子句做 know 的受詞，在該子句中當形容詞修飾 hat，whose hat 做 is 的補語】

Tell me ***which ones you want***. (告訴我哪些是你想要的。)

【which 引導名詞子句做 tell 的直接受詞，在該子句中 which ones 做 want 的受詞】

Tell me ***what books you have read recently***. (告訴我你最近讀過什麼書。)

【what 引導名詞子句做 tell 的直接受詞，在該子句中 what books 做 read 的受詞】

7. **疑問副詞：when, where, why, how** 在其所引導的子句中，**沒有代名作用**。(詳見 p.238)

名詞子句

When the meeting will be held has not been announced. 【when 引導名詞子句做主詞】
(會議什麼時候舉行尚未宣佈。)

名詞子句

Do you know ***when and where she was born***? 【when 和 where 引導名詞子句做 know 的受詞】
(你知道她是何時何地出生的嗎？)

That's ***where you are mistaken***. (那就是你錯誤的地方。)【where 引導名詞子句做主詞補語】

He went away without answering my question *where the post office was*. He may have

    been a mute.（他沒有回答我問的郵局在哪裡這問題就走掉了。他也許是個啞巴。）

【where 引導名詞子句，做 question 的同位語】

I wonder *why he hasn't come*.【why 引導名詞子句做 wonder 的受詞】

（我想知道他為何還沒來。）

Few people know *how hard he works*.【how 引導名詞子句做 know 的受詞】

（很少人知道他努力工作的程度。）

I have no idea as to *how it is done*.【how 引導名詞子句做介詞 to 的受詞】

（我不知道那是如何做的。）

8. **複合關係代名詞：what, whatever, whoever, whomever, whosever, whichever**（詳見 p.156）

What this country needs is great leaders.【what 引導名詞子句做主詞】

（這個國家所需要的是偉大的領導者。）

This is *what I want*.（這就是我想要的。）【what 引導名詞子句做主詞補語】

What(ever) you may do can't help him a bit.【what(ever) 引導名詞子句做主詞】

= *Anything that you may do* can't help him a bit.

（不管你做什麼都對他一點幫助也沒有。）

Whoever runs away is a coward.【whoever 引導名詞子句做主詞】

= *Anyone who runs away* is a coward.

（誰逃跑誰就是懦夫。）

Whichever (*of you*) *comes in first* will receive a prize.

= *The one* (*of you*) *that comes in first* will receive a prize.

（你們誰得第一誰就能得獎。）【whichever 引導名詞子句做主詞】

You may do *whatever you like*.【whatever 引導名詞子句做 do 的受詞】

= You may do *anything that you like*.

（你可做你所喜歡的任何事。）

You may give this pen to *whomever you like*.【whomever 引導名詞子句做介系詞 to 的受詞】

= You may give this pen to *anyone whom you like*.

（你可以把這枝筆送給你所喜歡的任何人。）

Return this notebook to *whosever name is on it*.【whosever 引導名詞子句做介系詞 to 的受詞】

= Return this notebook to *the one whose name is on it*.

（把這本筆記本還給名字寫在上面的人。）

【註 1】 **whatever** 和 **whichever** 也可當作**複合形容詞**，在所引導的名詞子句中，有形容詞

        作用。（詳見 p.158）

【註 2】 字尾有 **ever** 的關係代名詞亦可引導表讓步的副詞子句。

        Whoever else may object, I shall approve.【whoever 引導<u>副詞子句</u>】

           （不管誰反對，我都會贊成。）

        You may give this pen to *whoever wants it*.

           （你可以把這枝筆給任何想要它的人。）【whoever 引導<u>名詞子句</u>做介系詞 to 的受詞】

II. 引導形容詞子句的從屬連接詞

1. **關係代名詞：who, whom, whose, which, that**…等可用來引導形容詞子句（詳見 p.25, 149）

We found the boy *who was lost in the forest.*（我們找到了在森林中迷路的小男孩。）

Edison is an inventor *whose fame is world-wide.*（愛迪生是位世界有名的發明家。）

The package *which I posted* was for Mr. Chang.（我寄的那個包裹是給張先生的。）

He is the first American *that trod on Chinese soil.*（他是第一個踏上中國土地的美國人。）

2. **準關係代名詞：as, but, than** 也可引導形容詞子句（詳見 p.25, 159）

This is *the same* book *as I lost yesterday.*（這和我昨天遺失的那本書一樣。）【as 子句修飾 book】

There is *no one but admires her.*（沒有人不欽佩她。）【but 子句修飾 one】

He got *more* money *than he asked for.*（他得到比他要求更多的錢。）

3. **關係副詞：when, where, why, how** 也可引導形容詞子句（詳見 p.25, 242）

The day *when he was born* remains unknown.【when 子句是形容 day 的】
（他出生於哪一天依然不知道。）

I don't know the place *where you live.*（我不知道你所住的地方。）【where 子句是形容 place 的】

Tell me the reason *why you did not come.*（告訴我你沒來的理由。）【why 子句是形容 reason 的】

Do you know the way *he did it*?（你知道他做那件事的方法嗎？）
【the way he did it 源自 the way *how* he did it，可用 the way 或 how，或用 in which 代替；the way how 是古老的用法，現已不用】

【註】**after, before, since** 有時也可引導表時間的形容詞子句。

> The morning *after I arrived there*, I rambled into a wood of oaks.
> （在我到達那裡之後的第二天早上，我漫步走進了一片橡樹林。）
>
> The day *before you came* was rainy.（你來的前一天是雨天。）
>
> The uneventful period *since the election campaign ended* gave me an opportunity of looking back on the past.
> （從競選活動結束以來的這一段平靜無事的期間，給了我一個機會回顧過去。）

III. 引導副詞子句的從屬連接詞

1. **表時間的從屬連接詞：**

⑴ **when**（當…時候）（= **at** *or* **during the time that**）

I will come *when I am at leisure.*（我有空時會來。）

When the clock struck twelve, all the lights went out.
（當鐘敲十二點的時候，所有的燈都熄了。）

(2) **while**（當…時候）（= **during the time that**）

I'll think it over *while I am having my lunch*.（當我吃午餐時，我會好好地考慮一下。）

While the world lasts, human nature will remain what it is.
（只要世界存在，人性將永遠如此。）

You can sit down, *while I stand*.（當我站著的時候，你可以坐下。）

While I was studying, I fell asleep.（在我唸書時，我睡著了。）

I was watching TV *while my wife was cooking*.（當我太太做飯時，我正在看電視。）

(3) **as**（當…時候）

He trembled *as he spoke*.（當他說話時，他在發抖。）

Just as he was speaking there was a loud explosion.（正當他說話時，有一個很大的爆炸聲。）

【just 是副詞，修飾副詞子句以加強語氣】

【註】 when, while 和 as 的比較：

> **as** 的時間含義介於 when 和 while 之間，故有時依句意的時間長短，時間長者，as 可以等於 while；時間短者，as 可以等於 when。**when** 和 as 一樣，可以表「一點時間」或「一段時間」（= while）。**while** 只能表示「一段時間」，不能表示「一點時間」。

> He sang *as*（= *when*）*he worked*.（他一邊工作，一邊唱歌。）
> *As*（= *while*）*they were talking*, the rain began.
> （當他們在談話的時候，雨開始下了。）

> *While he received the bad news*, he almost fainted.【while 不能表「一點時間」】【誤】
> *When he received the bad news*, he almost fainted.【正】
> （當他接到那壞消息的時候，他幾乎昏倒了。）

> Please be quiet *while I am talking to you*.（當我對你們講話的時候，請安靜。）
> = Please be quiet *when I am talking to you*.【when 也可表「一段時間」】

when, while, as 都可以表示「一段時間」，如：

> *When* (*he was*) *a child*, he lived in Hong Kong.
> = *While* (*he was*) *a child*, he lived in Hong Kong.
> = *As* (*he was*) *a child*, he lived in Hong Kong.
> （當他是個小孩的時候，住在香港。）

但只有 as 可用於連接兩個逐漸發展或演變的動作或狀態。

We advance in experience *as we advance in years*.
（當我們隨著年歲的增長，經驗也增加了。）

⑷ **till**; **until**（一直到…爲止）

till 和 until 都含有連續的意思，兩字通用，其用法有三種：

① **till** 和 **until** 引導副詞子句接在含有 **come, finish, go, reach, return, start**…等，表一時性動作動詞的主要子句後面時，主要子句的動詞該用否定，即 not…till (until)。

I hope to finish the work *till* (or *until*) *he arrives.*【誤】
I hope to finish the work ***before*** *he arrives.*【正】
（我希望在他到達之前完成工作。）
I am afraid I can***not*** finish the work ***till*** (or ***until***) *he arrives.*【正】
I am afraid I can***not*** finish the work ***before*** *he arrives.*【正】
（我恐怕無法在他到達之前完成工作。）

I shall start *till* (or *until*) *he arrives.*【誤】
I shall not start ***till*** (or ***until***) *he arrives.*【正】
（我將不會開始，直到他到達。—— 我會在他到達後才開始。）
I shall start ***when*** *he arrives.*【正】
（我會在他到達時開始。）

② **till** 和 **until** 引導副詞子句接在**表持續性的動詞**如：**remain, stay, wait**…等後面時，主要子句的動詞該用肯定。

I remained there *till* (or ***until***) *he arrived.*（我留在那裡直到他到達。）
You may stay here *till* (or ***until***) *the rain stops.*（你可以留在這裡直到雨停爲止。）
I will wait *till* (or ***until***) *he comes.*（我要等到他來爲止。）

③ 在重複動詞來加強語氣的情形下，亦可用 **till** 或 **until** 來引導副詞子句。

We walked and walked ***until*** *it was dark.*（我們一直走，走到天黑爲止。）

【註 1】 在句首時，用 **until** 比 **till** 適當。

Until you told me, I had no idea of it.
（一直到你告訴我的時候爲止，關於那件事我全然不知。）
Until he went to college, he had never thought of his speech.
（在他進大學之前，他從未想過他說話的方式。）

【註 2】 在 **till** 或 **until** 所引導的子句中，不可用 **shall, will** 或 **would**。

He will wait *till* (or *until*) *I shall arrive.*【誤】
He will wait *till* (or *until*) *I arrive.*（他會一直等到我到達。）【正】

I shall wait *till* (or *until*) *he will arrive.*【誤】
I shall wait *till* (or *until*) *he arrives.*（我會一直等到他到達。）【正】

【註 3】 until 或 till 所引導的子句的主詞和主要子句的主詞相同時，until 或 till 子句中的主詞和 be 動詞可省略。

John, don't speak ***until*** (*you are*) *spoken to.*
（約翰，沒有人叫你發言之前，不要說話。）
He refused to leave his post ***until*** (*he was*) *ordered to do so.*
（未接到命令以前，他不肯離開工作崗位。）

【註 4】 **until** (till) 也可作介詞用。

> It was cold from Christmas *until* April.
> （從聖誕節到來年四月天氣很冷。）
> It was not *until* 2009 that he managed to finish his college work.
> （一直到 2009 年他才勉強完成他大學的學業。）

【註 5】 **not…until** 的句型變化。

> I did*n't* know it *until* (= before) *he came back*.
> 【在否定句中 until = before，not…until 是相關連接詞，until 子句修飾 not 作「直到…才」解】
>
> = It was *not until he came back* that I knew it.
> 【用「It is (was) + 強調部分 + 其餘部分」的公式加強句中的副詞部分 not until…，參照 p.115】
>
> = *Not until he came back* did I know it. 【否定副詞放在句首，句子要倒裝】
>
> = *Only when he came back* did I know it. 【only + 副詞（子句或片語），句子要倒裝】
> （直到他回來，我才知道那件事。）

⑤ **whenever**（無論何時）

Whenever Perry gets an idea for a novel, he jots it down in his notebook.
（每當派瑞想到一個寫小說的點子時，他就會記在他的筆記本上。）

I'll discuss it with you *whenever you like to come*.
（無論你喜歡什麼時候來，我都願意和你討論那件事。）

Whenever that man says "*To tell the truth*" I suspect that he's about to tell a lie.
（每當那人說「老實說…」的時候，我就懷疑他要說謊了。）

【註】 在口語中常用 **every time** 代替 **whenever**。

> You get younger *every time I see you*. （每當我見到你，都覺得你變得更年輕了。）
> You seem to have a ready-made answer, *every time I ask you a question*.
> （每當我問你問題時，你似乎都有現成的答案。）

⑥ **since**（自從…以來）：表時間的繼續。

I haven't seen John *since* he returned from Paris.
（自從約翰從巴黎回來，我還沒見過他。）

It is ten years *since* my father left home. （自從父親離開家已十年了。）

【註 1】 It 做主詞時，用 It is…since…，和 It has been…since…都可。用 is 是標準用法，
用 has been 是通俗的用法，也就是美國人現在的習慣用法。（參照 p.337）

> It *is* a year *since* he returned. 【正】【標準用法】
> It *has been* a year *since* he returned. 【正】【通俗用法】
> （他回來有一年了。）

【註2】 **since** 也可作介詞用，其受詞須爲一個指示特定時間（**a point of time**）而不是一段時間。

> I have lived here *since five months*.【誤】
> I have lived here *since five months ago*.【誤】【有些文法書誤以爲此句爲正確】
> （從五個月前我就住在這裡了。）
> I have lived here *for five months*.（我住在這裡五個月了。）【正】
> I have lived here *since January*.（我從一月起就住在這裡了。）【正】

【註3】 **since** 也可作副詞用，since 和完成式連用作「自那時起（= since then）」解，和簡單式連用作「以前（= ago）」解。（參照 p.247）

He caught (a) cold last Saturday and has been in bed ever *since*.
（他上週六感冒了，從那時起他就躺在床上。）

At first he refused but *since* has accepted.（起初他拒絕，但以後又接受了。）

The dog died *long since* (= *long ago*).（那隻狗很久以前就死了。）

He did it many years *since* (= *ago*).（他在許多年以前做那件事。）

⑺ **after**; **before**

A man should take a little rest *after he has worked hard*.
（一個人在他努力工作之後應該休息一下。）

Don't count your chickens *before they are hatched*.
（雞未孵出，莫預計其數；── 不要過早樂觀；不要打如意算盤。）

I'll do it *after I finish* (or *have finished*) *this work*.
（在我做完這件工作之後我將做那件事。）

That happened (*or* had happened) *before the war broke out*.
（那件事發生在戰爭爆發之前。）

【註1】 **before long**（不久）等於 **before a long time has passed**。（參閱 p.495）

I hope to see you *before long*.（我希望不久可以看到你。）
= I hope to see you *before a long time has passed*.

【註2】 **after**、**before** 也可作介詞用，在表示時間的用法時，**before** 不可接一段時間，須接一特定指示的時間。

A bright future is *before* him.（他面前有光明的未來。）

> I saw him *before a week*.【誤】
> Please come *before* five o'clock.【正】（請在五點以前來。）

The dog ran *after* a rabbit.（那隻狗追一隻兔子。）

Please line up one *after* another.（請一個接一個地排隊。）

after、**before** 也可作副詞用，after 作「以後；後來」解，before 作「在前；早於；以前」解。（參照 p.247）

Let me go in and you follow *after*.（讓我進去，你隨後跟著來。）

I never met him *before*. (我以前沒遇到過他。)

The show will begin at noon not *before*. (那表演在中午開始，不會早於中午。)

after 還可以作形容詞用，作「後來的 (= later)」解。

The *after* results of the storm were terrible. (那場暴風雨的後遺症非常可怕。)

In *after* years he regretted the mistakes of his boyhood.

(在晚年他後悔少年時期的錯誤。)

(8) **as** (*or* **so**) **long as** (= **while**) (在…的時候；只要)

You shall never enter this house *as long as* (= *while*) *I live in it.*

(在我住在這裡的時候，你永遠不許進入這屋子。)

As long as (= *while*) *I live*, you shall not want for anything.

(只要我仍然活著，你就不會缺乏任何東西。)

【註】**as** (*or* **so**) **long as** 也可引導副詞子句，表條件，等於 on condition that。

You can go where you like **so long as** (= *on condition that*) *you get back before dark.*

(你可以隨意到哪裡去，只要你在天黑以前回來。)

(9) **as often as** (= **whenever**; **each time**) (無論何時；每次)

Come *as often as you like.* (你什麼時候想來就來。)

We go to the movies *as often as we can.* (不論什麼時候只要能去，我們就會去看電影。)

As often as (= Each time) *I tried to get an answer from him*, he made some excuse and
avoided giving me the information I wanted.

(每當我想從他那裡得到答案的時候，他總是找個藉口避免給我所要的資料。)

(10) **once** (一旦；一…就…)

Once you see her, you will find what I say is true.

(你一見到她，就會發現我所說的是真的。)

Once printed, this dictionary will be very popular!【once 後省略 it is】

(當這字典出版時，會很受歡迎！)

Once a beast of prey has licked blood, it longs for it forever.

(當猛獸舐了血時，就永遠食髓知味了。)

【註】once 所引導的副詞子句可以同時為表時間和表條件。

Once you understand this rule, you will have no further difficulty.

= ① *As soon as you understand this rule*, you will have no further difficulty.

(你了解這規則，你就不會再有困難了。)【表時間】

② *If you once understand this rule*, you will have no further difficulty.

(你一旦了解這個規則，就不會再有困難。)【表條件】

⑾ **by the time (when)** = **by the time (that)** = before（在…之前）

　【大多指未來的時間，且 when 和 that 常常省略】

I will have left here ***by the time*** *you come back.*

（在你回來之前，我將已經離開這裡了。）

By the time *you get there*, it will be dark.（在你到達那裡之前，天就會黑了。）

⑿ **not…long before** (*or* **when**)（…不久，就…）：表「在…之前不久」。

It was ***not long before*** *I saw my mistake.*（不久我就看到我的錯誤了。）

= ***Soon*** I saw my mistake.【此類句子譯成中文時，**before 不要譯出**】

It will ***not*** be ***long before*** *he appears.*（他不久就會出現。）

I had ***not*** been ***long*** in that town ***when*** *the yellow fever broke out and killed the people by the hundreds.*（我在那城鎮住沒多久，黃熱病就發生了，死了好幾百人。）

【註 1】 **not…long before** 所表示的時間並未確定，若要表示一段確定的時間，則可以用確定時間代替。

　　 I had ***not*** waited ***two hours before*** *he appeared.*【用 two hours 代替 long】
　　 （我等不到兩小時，他就來了。）

　　 They had ***not*** been married ***a week before*** *they began to quarrel.*
　　 （他們結婚不到一週，就開始爭吵。）【用 a week 代替 long】

【註 2】 **long before** 作「過了很久才…」解，**before long** 作「不久」解。

　　 It was ***long before*** *he came.*（過了很久他才來。）
　　 We hope to hear from him ***before long***.（我們希望不久就能收到他的信。）

【註 3】 可以把 **not…long before** (*or* **when**) 中的 **long** 改為 **far** 或其他確定的距離，來表示距離。

　　 I had ***not*** gone ***far when*** *my horse began to limp.*
　　 （我走不遠馬就開始跛行了。）

　　 The thief had ***not*** run ***half a mile before*** *he was caught.*
　　 （小偷跑不到半哩遠，就被捉到了。）

【註 4】 not…long 之後用 before 或 when 在句意上沒有多大的差別；但在 It 做主詞時，不可用 **when**，只能用 before，因為用 when 無法造出有意義的句子。

　　 I had not waited long ***before*** (*or* ***when***) she appeared.
　　 〔在她出現之前（當她出現時），我沒等很久。—— 我等了不久，她就出現了。〕

　　 It will not be long $\left\{ \begin{array}{l} \textit{before}【正】 \\ \textit{when}【誤】 \end{array} \right\}$ spring comes.（春天不久就會來臨。）

(13) $\left\{\begin{array}{l}\textbf{hardly}\cdots\textbf{when}\ (or\ \textbf{before})\cdots\\\textbf{scarcely}\cdots\textbf{when}\ (or\ \textbf{before})\cdots\\\textbf{barely}\cdots\textbf{when}\ (or\ \textbf{before})\cdots\\\textbf{no sooner}\cdots\textbf{than}\end{array}\right\}$ (= as soon as) (一…就…)

在此種句型中，主要子句的動詞通常用**過去完成式**（**had + p.p.**），而副詞子句的動詞通常為**過去式**。過去完成式表示比過去先發生，但加上否定字 hardly, scarcely, barely, no sooner，表示「**幾乎沒有比…先發生**」，於是翻譯成「**一…就…**」。加強語氣時，可將 hardly, scarcely, barely, no sooner 放在句首形成倒裝句。(參照 p.629)

He had *hardly* arrived at the station *when* (*or before*) *the train began to leave.*
= *Hardly* had he arrived at the station *when* (*or before*) *the train began to leave.*
（ 他一到車站，火車就開動了。 ）

英美用法中，亦有主要子句的動詞用現在完成式，而副詞子句的動詞用現在式的情形。因為現在完成式比現在式先發生，同樣再以否定字 hardly, scarcely, barely, no sooner 將前後的時間拉近。

No sooner **has** any important character **wandered** on to an airfield *than a suitable aircraft*
comes *roaring up.*
（ 每當任何重要人物漫步到機場來時，就會有一架相配的飛機隆隆地滑行過來。 ）

【註】**hardly** 和 **scarcely** 是表否定的副詞，可以 **not…before** 的句型互換。

I had *scarcely* waited an hour *when he appeared.*
= I had *not* waited an hour *before he appeared.* （ 我等了不到一個小時他就出現了。 ）

(14) $\left\{\begin{array}{l}\textbf{as soon as}\\\textbf{directly}\ (\textbf{when})\\\textbf{immediately}\ (\textbf{when}\ or\ \textbf{after})\\\textbf{the moment}\ (\textbf{that})\\\textbf{the instant}\ (\textbf{that})\\\textbf{the minute}\ (\textbf{that})\end{array}\right\}$ (一…就)

directly 和 immediately 都是副詞，當連接詞用，與 when 連用視為連接詞片語。或可視 directly 仍為副詞，修飾連接詞 when。the moment, the instant, the minute 都是名詞當連接詞，後面可接 that，但通常省略；**此類連接詞顯然是由 at the moment when, at the instant when 和 at the minute when 演變而來。**

She wept aloud *as soon as she heard the news.* （ 她一聽到那消息就大聲地哭。 ）

As soon as the party was over, Lucy got her coat and ran down the street to meet her father.
（ 當宴會一結束，露西就拿起她的外套並且跑到街上去和她的父親見面。 ）

Directly I had done it, I knew I had made a mistake. （ 我一做完了，就知道我做錯了。 ）

Immediately (*when*) *the button was pressed*, the mine exploded. （一按鈕，地雷就爆炸。）

The moment (*that*) *I saw you*, I knew you were angry with me.

= *At the moment when I saw you*, I knew you were angry with me.

（我一見到你，就知道你在生我的氣。）

The instant he opened the door, a dog ran in. （他一開門，狗就跑進來。）

= *At the instant when he opened the door*, a dog ran in.

I'll tell him the news *the minute* (*that*) *he arrives*.

= I'll tell him the news *at the minute when he arrives*.

（他一到，我就會告訴他那個消息。）

【註 1】 **as soon as** 所引導的子句不可用進行式。

She opened the door *as soon as she was hearing the knock*. 【誤】【不可用進行式】

She opened the door *as soon as she heard the knock*. 【正】

（她一聽到敲門聲，就打開門。）

【註 2】 **so soon as** 的語氣比 **as soon as** 重一些。

I came *as soon as I heard of it*. 【語氣較輕】

I came *so soon as I heard of it*. 【語氣較重】

（我一聽到這件事就來了。）

【註 3】 **as soon as** 所引導的副詞子句也可改為 **on + 動名詞（V-ing）**的形式。

He started *as soon as he received the news*.

= *On receiving the news*, he started.

（他一接到消息就出發了。）

【註 4】 第(13)項所列的表時間連接詞片語，和第(14)項所列的表時間連接詞片語，在意義上都作
「一…就…」解，故可以互相代換。

He had *no sooner* sat down *than* he fell asleep.

= He had { *scarcely* / *hardly* / *barely* } sat down *when* (*or before*) he fell asleep.

= { *As soon as* / *Directly* (*when*) / *Immediately* (*when or after*) / *The moment* (*that*) / *The instant* (*that*) / *The minute* (*that*) } he sat down, he fell asleep.

（他一坐下，就睡著了。）

$$
(15)\begin{cases}
\textbf{any time} = \textbf{whenever}（任何時候）\\
\textbf{every time}（每次）\\
\textbf{each time}（每當…的時候）\\
\textbf{next time}（下次）\\
\textbf{last time}（上次）\\
\textbf{the day}（當…那天）
\end{cases}
$$

***Any time** he likes to come*, I will see him.（無論何時他想來，我都願意見他。）

She smiles ***every time** she sees me.*（她每次見到我都笑。）

***Each time** he failed*, he made up his mind to try harder again.
（每當他失敗的時候，他就下定決心要再更努力。）

***Next time** I see you*, I will show you my new dress.
（下次我見到你，我會把我的新衣服給你看。）

***Last time** I saw him*, he said he was going to Hong Kong.
（上次我見到他，他說正要去香港。）

***The day** her husband died*, she gave birth to a son.
（當她丈夫死的那天，她生下了一個兒子。）

2. 表地點的從屬連接詞：

(1) **where**（在…地方；到…地方）

Apricots won't grow ***where** the winters are cold.*（冬天很冷的地方杏樹不會生長。）

***Where** there is no rain*, farming is difficult or impossible.
（沒有雨水的地方，耕作是很困難，或者是不可能的。）

【註】where…there 中 where = if 是引導表「條件」的副詞子句。
　　　***Where**（= **If**）there is a will, there is a way.*（有志者事竟成。）

(2) **wherever**（任何地方）：與 anywhere, everywhere 同義。

She follows him ***wherever** he goes.*（她跟著他走到任何地方。）

= She follows him ***to any place where** he goes.*　【複合關係副詞 wherever 本身修飾動詞 follows 也修飾動詞 goes】

He is welcomed ***wherever** he goes.*（他無論到什麼地方，都很受歡迎。）

We will meet ***wherever** the committee decides.*
（委員會決定在什麼地方開會，我們就在什麼地方開會。）

Sit ***wherever** you like.*（你喜歡坐在什麼地方，就坐在什麼地方。）

【註】**wherever** 可和 **may** 連用，引導表讓步的副詞子句，等於 "no matter where"。

表讓步的 wherever 亦可用 where 代替。

Wherever you may go, you cannot succeed without perseverance.

= *No matter where you may go*, you cannot succeed without perseverance.

（無論你到任何地方，沒有毅力是不會成功的。）

Go where you may, you still find yourself in a conditional world.

（無論你到哪裡，你仍會發現自己處在有限制的世界裡。）【可以用 where 代替 wherever】

(3) **whence** (= to the place from which)（從…地方）

To climb back *whence I came* was impossible.（要爬回我出發的地方是不可能的。）

They returned *whence they came*.（他們回到他們所來的地方。）

(4) $\left\{ \begin{array}{l} \textbf{everywhere (that)} \\ \textbf{anywhere (that)} \end{array} \right\}$ (= **wherever**)（無論什麼地方）

Everywhere you go, I go too.（凡你所到之處我也去。）

You may go *anywhere you like*.（你喜歡去哪裡就去哪裡。）

3. 表狀態的從屬連接詞：

(1) **as**（像；依照）

Do it *as I do*.（照我那樣去做它。）

Do in Rome *as the Romans do*.（入境隨俗 —— 在羅馬要按照羅馬人的做法。）

You should pronounce the new words you learn *as your teacher does*.

（你對所學的生字要照老師的發音來唸。）

Do to others *as you would have others do to you*.（己所欲，施於人。）

You must do it *just as I have done it*.【just 修飾 as，能加強語氣】

（你必須完全照我做那件事的方式來做。）

【註 1】從屬子句 *as is often the case*; *as is usual with sb.*; *as is the custom with sb.*; *as is supposed*; *as is anticipated*; *as is natural*; *as is hoped* 等之中的 **as** 可視為關係代名詞，相當於 **which**，引導形容詞子句（參閱 p.160）；亦可視為表狀態的連接詞引導副詞子句，此時 as 後面的 **it** 省略了。比較下面兩種不同的文法解釋：

He was late for school, *as* (= *which*) *was usual with him*.　形容詞子句

（他上課遲到了，他經常如此。）【as 可視為關係代名詞】

He was late for school, *as* (*it*) *was usual with him*.　副詞子句【as 也可視為連接詞，it 省略】

【註2】 在 *as follows*, *as regards*, *as concerns* 等從屬子句中，*follows*, *regards*, *concerns* 都是動詞，只是 **as** 後面的 **it** 省略罷了。其中 *as regards*, *as concerns* 現已當成介系詞的片語，相當於 *about*。注意這三個動詞的此種用法已經變為成語，不論主要子句的主詞是單數或複數，動詞現在或過去，都用第三人稱單數現在式的形式。

He made the statements *as follows*. (他發表聲明如下。)

Their names are *as follows*. (他們的名字如下。)

The terms and stipulations are *as follows*. (條件規定如下。)

The reply will run *as follows*. (回答將是下面這樣。)

Just before the battle, the general addressed his army *as follows*.
(在開戰前不久，將軍對他的軍隊訓話如下。)

His words were *as follows*. (他說的話如下。)

As regards this journey, we can now decide nothing.
(關於這次旅行，我們現在不能做任何決定。)

As concerns me, he might leave his door wide open.
(就我而言，他可以讓門大開著。)

【註3】 **as** 後面也有接名詞或形容詞的情形，實際上是一個省略句，文法上視為主詞或受詞補語，即 as 前後的名詞指同一人或同一事物，as 後的形容詞則修飾 as 前面的名詞。此種用法的 as 多用在：look upon, treat, regard, speak of, think of, recognize, look down upon, refer to, acknowledge 等意義相近的動詞之後。

Those students *look upon* the teacher *as* their father.【their father 當受詞補語】
= Those students *look upon* the teacher *as if he were* their father.
(學生把這位老師當作他們的父親看待。)

I *look upon* it *as* certain.【certain 當受詞補語】
= I *look upon* it *as if it were* certain. (我認為那是確實的。)

He *treats* me *as* a stranger.【a stranger 當受詞補語】
= He *treats* me *as if I were* a stranger.
(他待我猶如對待一個陌生人一樣。)

We *regard* him *as* an honest man.【an honest man 當受詞補語】
(我們認為他是一個誠實的人。)

People *speak of* Mark Twain *as* the most humorous writer of all times.
(人們稱馬克吐溫為古今最幽默的作家。)
【the most humorous writer of all times 當受詞補語】

The people of America *think of* Lincoln *as* a friend of freedom.
(美國人民認為林肯是自由之友。)【a friend of freedom 當受詞補語】

I do not *recognize* her *as* his lawful wife.
(我不承認她是他的合法妻子。)【his lawful wife 當受詞補語】

They *look down upon* him *as* a sort of dependent.
(他們看不起他，把他看成寄生蟲。)【a sort of dependent 當受詞補語】

Don't *refer to* your sister *as* a silly cow.【a silly cow 當受詞補語】

（別把你妹妹說成是傻瓜。）

【注意 1】　consider 一般用法不加 as，而用 to be，to be 也可省略。

Most people *considered* him (*to be*) a fool.

（大多數的人認為他是個傻瓜。）

【注意 2】　上面例句中的 regard…as, recognize…as, look upon…as, 等都譯為「認為…是」，refer to…as, speak of…as 譯為「把…稱為…」，treat…as 譯為「把…當作…對待」。**as 之後的名詞或形容詞是當受詞的補語。**此種句型改成被動式後為 be thought of as, be looked upon as, be regarded as 等譯為「被認為是…」，be referred to as, be spoken of as 譯為「被稱為…」，be treated as 譯為「被當作…看待」。**此時 as 之後的名詞或形容詞為主詞的補語。**

He *is regarded as* the best dentist in town.

（他被認為是城內最好的牙醫師。）【the best dentist 當主詞補語】

Books and magazines *are* often *referred to as* mental food.

（書報雜誌常被人們稱為精神食糧。）【mental food 當主詞補語】

Lincoln *is thought of as* a friend of freedom.

（林肯被認為是自由之友。）【a friend of freedom 當主詞補語】

He *is* universally *acknowledged as* an authority.

（世人認為他是權威。）【an authority 當主詞補語】

He *is treated as* a servant.【a servant 當主詞補語】

（他受到像僕人一般的對待。）

【註 4】有時 as 後的主詞和 be 動詞省略，而形成 *as usual*, *as possible*, *as always*, *as now*, *as before*, *as ever*, *as elsewhere* 等慣用語。

I went to school *as usual*.（我像往常一樣上學。）

= I went to school *as it was usual*.

Come as soon *as possible*.（儘快過來。）

= Come as soon *as it is possible*.

John, *as always*, went to the movies alone.

（約翰像往常一樣獨自去看電影。）

【as always 是由 as *it* always *is* 省略而來】

In those days, *as now*, most of these people were tall and very powerful.

（當時和現在一樣，這些人大多是非常高而且有力的。）

【as now 是由 as *they are* now 省略而來】

Soon the rock was left dry *as before*.（不久岩石便如以前一般的乾燥了。）

【as before 是由 as *it was* before 省略而來】

(2) **(just) as⋯, so⋯（像⋯那樣；猶如）**

> **as 是連接詞，引導副詞子句修飾後面的相關副詞 so**。若要加強語氣時，可在 as 前加 just；
> so 後的主要子句可以倒裝，即把助動詞或 be 動詞放在主詞前。此種句子的中文譯法，最好
> 先譯 so 後的主要子句。

副詞子句修飾副詞 so

As I would not be a slave, so I would not be a master.　| as⋯so
　‖　　　　　　　　　　　　　　　‖　　　主　要　子　句　| 成雙成對出現
句意上等於 According as　　　　　　　in that same way

（我不願做主人，就像我不願做奴隸一樣。）【as 引導副詞子句，修飾它的相關修飾詞 so】

As two is to one, so twelve is to six.（12：6＝2：1）

As you sow, so will you reap.（要怎麼收穫，先怎麼栽；種瓜得瓜。）

As you make your bed, so must you lie on it.（自作自受。）

As you brew, so you drink.（自作自受。）

Just as some people are born artists, so some are born sportsmen.

（有些人是天生的運動家，就像有些人是天生的藝術家一樣。）

【Just 是副詞，修飾 as 所引導的副詞子句】

As lungs are to the animals, so leaves are to the plants.

（葉子之於植物，猶如肺之於動物。）

As men live, so they die.

（人會死，就如人能活著一樣。── 有生必有死。）

【註】表示 A：B＝C：D 的句型共有

主要句型
- **A is to B as C is to D.**
- ＝ **A is to B what C is to D.**【what 子句是 A is 的補語】
- ＝ **As C is to D, so A is to B.**【so 之後的主詞和動詞可倒裝】

導來句型
- ＝ **What C is to D, that is A to B.**【what 子句放在前面，做 that 的同位語】
- ＝ **What C is to D, A is to B.**【what 子句放在前面】
- ＝ **A stands to B as C stands to D.**【動詞 is 改為 stands】
- ＝ **As C stands to D, so A stands to B.**【動詞 is 改為 stands】
- ＝ **A is among B what C is among D.**【介詞 to 可改為 among 等】
- ＝ **A is to B the same thing as C is to D.**【用 the same thing as 代替 as】
- ＝ **A is to B the relation that C is to D.**【用 the relation that 代替 as】

（A 之於 B，猶如 C 之於 D。）

例：

> Water *is to* fishes *as* air *is to* men.
> = Water *is to* fishes *what* air *is to* men.
> = *As* air *is to* men, *so* water *is to* fishes.

　　　【主要子句可倒裝成 so is water to fishes】

> = *What* air *is to* men, *that is* water *to* fishes.
> = *What* air *is to* men, water *is to* fishes.
> = Water *stands to* fishes *as* air *stands to* men.
> = *As* air *stands to* men, *so* water *stands to* fishes.
> = Water *is among* fishes *what* air *is among* men.
> = Water *is to* fishes *the same thing as* air *is to* men.
> = Water *is to* fishes *the relation that* air *is to* men.

　　（水之於魚，猶如空氣之於人。）

(3) $\begin{cases} \textbf{as if} \\ = \textbf{as though} \end{cases}$ （好像；宛如）

as if 和 as though 意義相同，但 as if 較常用。(詳見 p.371)

The child talks ***as if*** *he were a man*. （那孩子談吐宛如一個大人似的。）

He talks ***as though*** *he knew all about it*. （他談話的樣子好像他知道全部的情形。）

He speaks English ***as if*** *he were an Englishman*. （他說起英語來好像是個英國人。）

Jack nodded sagely, ***as though*** *he understood every word*.

（傑克聰慧地點著頭，宛如他明白了每一句話似的。）

He lives ***as if*** *he were a millionaire*. （他生活得好像是個百萬富翁。）

4. 表比較的從屬連接詞：

(1) **than** （比）：表示差異的連接詞。(詳見 p.200「形容詞的比較方式」)

He works harder ***than*** *his master* (*works*). （他比他的主人更努力工作。）

【than 是連接詞，引導省略 works 的副詞子句修飾副詞 harder】

He treated me more like a stranger ***than*** *like a friend*.

（他對待我與其說像一位朋友，不如說像一位陌生人。）

【than 是連接詞，引導省略 he treated me 的副詞子句】

Tom is taller ***than*** *Paul*. （湯姆比保羅還高。）

His mother is more kind ***than*** *intelligent*.

（他的母親與其說是聰明，不如說是仁慈。）

(2) the…the…（越…越…）：與比較級的形容詞或副詞連用。（詳見 p.245 關係副詞 the）

副詞┌子句┐

The *sooner you do it,* the better it will be. （你越早做那件事越好。）

【第一個 the 是關係副詞引導副詞子句，修飾第二個 the（指示副詞）。本句可省略主詞和動詞，而變成 The sooner, the better.】

副詞┌子句┐

The *happier a human being is,* the longer he lives. （人越快樂，就活得越久。）

The *more you eat,* the fatter you will get. （你吃得越多，將變得越胖。）

The *more you work,* the more you earn. （你工作越多，賺得也越多。）

The *harder you work,* the sooner you will finish.
（你工作越努力，你就越快完成。）

【註1】 有時可在主要子句的主詞前面加 **do** 表示加強語氣。

The *more one learns,* the easier **do** things become.
（越有學問，越明事理。）

The *farther we proceed,* the more difficulties **do** we meet.
（我們越是深入，所碰到的困難也越多。）

【註2】 「the + 比較級…, the + 比較級」在句意明確時，常以省略句的形式出現。

The *sooner* (*you do it*), **the better** (*it will be*).
（越快越好。）【括弧中主詞和動詞被省略】

The *smaller* the mind (*is*), **the greater** the conceit (*will be*).
（心胸越小，就越自大。）【省略動詞】

The *more brilliant* the diamond (*is*), **the better** (*it will look*).
（鑽石越亮越好。）【省略 is 和 it will look】

The *nearer* the church (*is to your home*), **the further** from God (*you will be*).
（離教堂越近，就離上帝越遠。—— 諷刺語）【省略 is to your home 和 you will be】

The *more,* **the better**.
（越多越好。）【省略主詞和動詞】

The *fewer* the words (*are said*), **the better** the prayer (*sounds*).
（祈禱者的話越少越好。）【省略動詞】

The *more,* **the merrier**. （多多益善。）【省略主詞和動詞】

More haste, *less* speed.
（欲速則不達。）【省略 the 和動詞】

The *nearer* the bone, **the sweeter** the meat.
（越靠近骨頭的肉，味道越美。）【省略動詞】

【註3】 關係副詞所引導的副詞子句和其他副詞子句一樣，在句意需要時可由對等連接詞連接。

The *smaller the room* **or** *the more people in it,* the faster the air becomes bad.
（房間越小，或是越多人在裡面，房裡的空氣就越快變壞。）

【註 4】 有時可把主要子句放在副詞子句的前面。

I sing the worse, *the more I practice*.（我越練習，就唱得越糟。）

副詞子句

= *The more I practice*, the worse I sing.【the worse 是為了接近修飾語才放在前面】

關係副詞（＝By how much）　指示副詞（＝by so much）

從此例句中可看出，the 在比較級形容詞或副詞前為指示副詞，作「到⋯的程度」解釋。**指示副詞 the 可單獨使用**，關係副詞 the 為連接詞，所以不可單獨使用。再看下面例句，更為明白。

If you start now, you will be back *the* sooner.（如果你現在出發，你將回來得更快。）
‖
by so much

⑶ **how**（＝ **in the manner that**; **as**）（照⋯的樣子）

You should behave *how your father does*.（你應該以你父親的行為做榜樣。）
I have a right to spend my money *how I please*.
（我有權照我喜歡的樣子花我的錢。）

⑷ **according as**（依照）

We can earn more or less *according as we work*.
（我們賺得多或少，要視我們工作而定。）

You may take an oral or written exam *according as you prefer*.
（你可以隨你的喜好考口試或筆試。）

The business will prosper *according as it is judiciously managed*.
（企業是否成功，要靠它適當的管理。）

The thermometer rises or falls *according as the air is hot or cold*.
（溫度計是隨著空氣的熱或冷而升降。）

He is happy or sad *according as he has money or not*.
（他是高興或是悲傷，視他有沒有錢而定。）

【註 1】 according as 為連接詞片語，引導副詞子句；according to 和 in accordance with 為片語介詞，後面接名詞（片語）為受詞。

副詞子句

You will be praised or blamed *according as your work is good or bad*.
（你會受到稱讚或責備，都依你的工作的好壞而定。）

副詞片語

According to the weather report, it will be fine tomorrow.
（根據氣象報告，明天天氣會很好。）

【註2】 according as 除去作「依照」解，還可作「如果」解。

According as I have the money, I'll go. (如果我有錢我就去。)
= *If* I have the money, I'll go.

(5)
{ **in proportion as**
in ratio as } (按…比例；愈…愈…)

In proportion as a country grows in wealth, it will cease to delight in war.
(國愈富則愈厭惡戰爭。)

We gain skill *in proportion as we practice*. (我們隨練習而獲得技巧。——熟能生巧。)

【註】 *in proportion as* 為連接詞片語引導副詞子句；*in proportion to* 為片語介詞，後面接
名詞（片語）為受詞。

副詞子句
Men are happy *in proportion as they are virtuous*. (道德愈高尚的人就愈幸福。)

副詞片語
They made contributions *in proportion to their wealth*. (他們按財富的多寡來捐獻。)

(6) **as…as**（像…一樣）

第一個 as 為副詞，修飾其後的副詞或形容詞，**第二個 as 為連接詞，引導副詞子句修飾第一個**
as。as 所引導的副詞子句常以省略句的形式出現。(參閱 p.200)

Tom is as tall *as Paul* (*is*). (湯姆和保羅一樣高。)【省略 is】

This is *two and a half times as* heavy *as that*. (這個有那個的二倍半重。)

Mary is as beautiful *as* (*she is*) *kind*. (瑪麗旣漂亮又仁慈。)

We walked as far *as our legs could carry us*. (我們的腿能走多遠就走多遠。)

【註1】 as 子句如果因省略而導致句意混淆時，則不可省略。

{ It is as cold *as it was yesterday*.【正】(天氣像昨天一樣冷。)
It is as cold *as it*.【誤】【句意不明】

{ We ran as fast *as we could*.【正】(我們盡力地快跑。)
We ran as fast *as we*.【誤】【句意不明】

We can run as fast *as they* (*can run*).【正】
(我們能跑得像他們一樣快。)

【註2】 *as still as still* 是後面省略了 can (*or* could) be 的慣用語，意為「寂靜到不能再寂靜
的程度」，第二個 still 是形容詞當名詞用，以加強語氣。其他類似片語有 as hard as
hard, as true as true, as clear as clear,…等。

(7) {
　not so (as)…as（不像…那樣）
　no…so (as)…as（沒有…像…那樣）
}

表示不同等之比較。as…as 原是用於表同等之比較，但現代英語中，尤其是日常會話中，也常用 as…as 來表示不同等之比較。即 as…as 可用於肯定或否定，而 so…as 只能用於否定。在此句型中，後面的 as 爲連接詞引導副詞子句修飾前面的相關副詞 so 或 as。

This work is *not so* (or *as*) easy *as you think*.（這項工作並不如你想像的那樣容易。）

Nothing is *so* (or *as*) precious *as health*.（沒有東西比健康寶貴。）

No person is either *so* happy or *so* unhappy *as he imagines* (*he is*).

（沒有人如他所想像的那樣幸福或不幸福。）

He is *not so* fond of work *as* (*he is fond*) *of play*.

（他不像喜歡遊戲一樣地喜歡工作。）【包含介詞的動詞片語，最後的介詞不可省略】

【**註 1**】下列句子中，as 所引導的子句可省略。

　　He has *as many* (*as I have*).（他也有那樣多。）
　　I thought *as much* (*as this comes to*).（我也是認爲那樣多。）
　　I can do it *as well* (*as you can*).（我也能做。）
　　It may be *as well* here to mention (*as not*).（在這裡提不提都可以。）

【**註 2**】在兩種比較同時進行時，第二個 as 可省略。

{
　Tom is as young (*as*) or younger than John.
　= Tom is as young as John or younger.
　（湯姆像約翰一樣或更年輕。）
}

{
　He is fully as tall (*as*) if not taller than his older brother.
　= He is fully as tall as, if not taller than, his older brother.
　= He is fully as tall as his older brother, if not taller.
　（他即使不比他哥哥高，也和他哥哥一樣高。）
}

5. 表原因的從屬連接詞：

(1) **as**（因爲）：引導副詞子句，通常放在主要子句之前。

As it was getting very late, we soon turned back.（因爲時間很晚，所以我們很快就往回走。）

As there is no school, I shall be at home.（因爲沒有課，所以我將會待在家裡。）

As he was such a fool, I refused to listen to him.

（因爲他是那樣一個傻瓜，所以我拒絕聽他的。）

As you are evidently very busy, I will not waste your time.

（因爲你顯然很忙，所以我不願意浪費你的時間。）

【註】 當 **as** 所表示的原因已爲對方所知時，其所引導的子句也可以放在主要子句之後。

You need not go with me, *as you are busy*. 【原因對方已知】

（你不必陪我去，因爲你很忙。）

> I cannot go with you, *as I am busy*. 【不佳 —— 原因對方未知】
> *As I am busy*, I cannot go with you. 【佳】
> （因爲我很忙，所以我不能陪你去。）

⑵ **because**（**因爲**）：引導副詞子句表示直接的原因。

The crops failed, *because there was too much rain*.

（農作物歉收，因爲雨量過多。）

The light went out, *because the oil was out*. （因爲油沒有了，所以燈就熄了。）

I did not go out *because it rained*. （因爲下雨，所以我沒出去。）

Because he has faults, I love him the better.

（因爲他有缺點，我更加愛他。）

【註 1】 because 用在否定句時，否定字 **not** 可能修飾動詞，也可能修飾 because 所引導的
副詞子句。同樣的一句話，卻有兩種不同的含意。

I did **not** go *because I was afraid*.

此時 not 修飾 go，則譯成「我沒有去，因爲我害怕。」

（= I didn't go, and the reason was fear.）

I did **not** go *because I was afraid*.

此時 not 修飾 because 子句，則譯成「我不是因爲怕才去的。」

（= I went, but the reason was not fear.）

有時依句意可明顯看出只有一種含意合理，另一種含意不可能存在。

He did **not** come *because he wanted to see me*. （他並非因爲要見我而來。）

【not 如修飾 come，則譯爲「他不能來，因爲他要見我。」顯然是不合常理的句子】

He can **not** go to school *because he is sick*. （他因生病不能來上學。）

【not 如修飾 because 子句，則譯爲「他不是因爲生病才來上學。」顯然是不合常理的句子】

如果 because 的前面有逗點（ , ），則 not 必爲修飾動詞。

I did **not** go, *because I was afraid*. （我沒有去，因爲我害怕。）

【註2】 在 "**The reason is**⋯" 之後通常接 **that** 子句。但口語中有時也用 "The reason is because⋯" 此種用法較不正式。

> **The reason** she refused to go **was that** she had no money.
> = She refused to go **because** she had no money.
> （她拒絕去是因為她沒錢。）

> ⎰ **The reason** (why) I love him **is that** he has a perfect character. 【正式】
> ⎱ **The reason** (why) I love him **is** *because* he has a perfect character. 【不正式】
> 　（我愛他是因為他有完美的人格。）

【註3】 because of 是片語介詞，後接名詞（片語）；because 是連接詞，後接子句。

> I did not go **because of** rain. （我因為下雨而沒去。）
> = I did not go **because** it rained.

【註4】 在中文裡常常說「因為⋯所以」，因此很多人習慣性地把表原因的 because, as 或 since 和 so 誤用在同一個句子中。**在英文中這兩個子句，只能用一個連接詞。**

> ⎰ *Because* he was careless, *so* he failed. 【誤】
> ⎪ He failed **because** *he was careless*. 【正】
> ⎱ He was careless, *so* he failed. 【正】
> 　（他因疏忽而失敗。）

> ⎰ *As* he did not study hard, *so* he has failed again. 【誤】
> ⎪ 【連接詞重複，亦不適合 As⋯, so⋯之句型】
> ⎪ **As** *he did not study hard*, he has failed again. 【正】
> ⎱ He did not study hard, *so he has failed again*. 【正】
> 　（他因為不用功，所以又不及格了。）

> ⎰ *Since* you do not understand, *so* I will explain again. 【誤】
> ⎱ **Since** *you do not understand*, I will explain again. 【正】
> 　（既然你不懂，我會再解釋一次。）

(3) ⎰ **inasmuch as** ⎱ （**因為**）：與 since 意義相當。
　 ⎱ **in as much as** ⎰

He knows the truth *inasmuch as* *he was there*.
（因為他在場，所以他知道實情。）

In as much as *the debtor has no property*, I abandoned the claim.
（因為債務人無財產，所以我放棄了債權。）

He knows the secret *inasmuch as* *she has told him*.
= *Since* *she has told him*, he knows the secret.
（因她已告訴了他，他知道那件秘密。）

⑷ **now that**（= since）（因為；既然）

Now that we have gone so far, we might go a little further.

（我們既然走了這麼遠，我們還可以再走遠一點。）

Now that you are here, you'd better stay. （既然你到這裡了，最好留下來。）

Now that you have finished your work, you may go.

（既然你已做完你的工作，你可以走了。）

Now that you are a big boy, you must behave better.

（你既然是個大孩子了，你的行為必須檢點些。）

"*Now that we have got liberty*," they said, "we may do whatever we like."

（「既然我們已獲得了自由，」他們說，「我們就可以做我們喜歡的事。」）

【註】 now that 在口語裡常把 that 省略，只用 now 來當連接詞。此種用法中的 "now" 已經
不再表示時間觀念的「現在」了，而與 as, since 有相同的意義。

Now (*that*) *you are well again*, you can travel.

（既然你已康復了，你可以旅行。）

⑸ seeing (**that**)
considering (**that**) }= since （因為；鑒於）：表示原因已為對方所知時使用。（參照 p.511）

Seeing (*that*) *she is a mere child*, it is not safe to let her go alone.

（她既然只是個小孩，讓她單獨去是不安全的。）

He has no right to vote, *seeing* (*that*) *he is a minor*.

（他無權投票，因為他未成年。）

Considering (*that*) *I have told you three times*, you must know it.

（鑒於我已告訴你三次，你一定知道這件事了。）

Considering (*that*) *he is a boy*, I forgive his bad manners.

（考慮到他是個孩子，我原諒他的無禮。）

⑹ in that （因為）
for that （由於；因為）

in that 等於 in the fact that（因…事實）相當於 because，在現代英語中多用 because 代替。
for that 的意義與 for 相當，但較少用。

In that he is ill, he feels unable to do it. （因為他生病，他覺得不能做那件事。）

Men differ from brutes *in that they can think and speak*.

（人與獸類之區別在於人能思考和說話。）

For that he is honest, we all like him. （由於他很誠實，我們大家都喜歡他。）

(7) **since**（**因為；既然**）：語氣比 because 稍弱，但比 as 稍強，常放在句首。

I will come, *since you ask me*. （既然你要求我，我會來的。）

Since we have no money, we can't buy it. （因為我們沒錢，所以我們不能買它。）

Since that is so, there is no more to be said. （既然如此，也沒話可說了。）

Since you said so, I believed it to be true. （既然你這樣說，我就相信那是真的。）

【註】 **because, as, since** 的比較。

　　because, as, since 三者都可作「因為」解，其中 because 的語氣最重，其次為 since，as 最弱，但一般用法並沒有多大差別。在回答 **why** 引導的疑問句時，必須用 **because**。

"*Why* is gold so valuable?" （黃金為何那樣有價值？）

"*Because* gold is very scarce." （因為黃金很稀少。）

在原因很明顯或原因為對方已知時，多使用 **as, since**。

As it's raining, you'd better take a taxi.
（因為在下雨，你最好搭計程車。）

在口語中用 **because** 語氣較強，較不客氣；用 **as** 語氣較柔和，較有禮貌。

I will come *because you request it*. 【較不客氣】
（因為你要求，我才來。）

As you request it, I will come. 【較有禮貌】
（因為你的要求，我會來。）

(8) **when**（= **since**; **considering that**）（**既然；鑒於**）

How can I help them to understand *when they won't listen to me*?
（既然他們不聽我的話，我怎麼能幫助他們了解呢？）

I can't tell you anything *when you won't listen*.
（既然你不願意聽，我就不說什麼了。）

(9) *it is* **that**（= **because**）（**是因為**）

If I find fault, it is *that I want you to do better in the future*.
　　　　　　　　‖
　　　　　　　because
（如果我指責你的缺點，那是因為我要你將來做得更好。）
【表原因的 that 子句，和 because 子句一樣，可做主詞補語】

If you hate him, it is *that he is brighter than you*.
　　　　　　　‖
　　　　　　because
（如果你討厭他，那是因為他比你聰明。）

⑩ **not because…but because…**（不是因為…而是因為…）

I eat vegetables *not because I like them but because they are good for the health.*

（我吃蔬菜不是因為喜歡蔬菜而吃，而是因為有益健康而吃。）

We rented the house *not because we like it, but because there was no other house to let.*

（我們租那間房子不是因為我們喜歡它，而是因為沒有其他房子出租。）

【註1】 上面連接詞片語，事實上就是由對等連接詞 not…but 連接兩個 because 子句，所以當然 not…but 也可連接兩個 because of 的片語。

副 詞 片 語

The ship was delayed *not because of the war, **but** because of a snowstorm.*

（這船不是因為戰爭而延誤，而是因為暴風雪。）

【註2】 下面句型都是和 not because…but because 相同的句型。

> not that not…but (because)
> not but that…but because
> not but what…but because
> not that…but that

They didn't exchange even a single word, ***not that** they did**n't** know each other,* ***but** they were in low spirits then.*

（他們彼此之間連一句話也沒有交談，並非因為他們互相不認識，而是因為他們當時情緒都不佳。）

It is ***not that** I am unwilling **but that** I have no time.*

（不是因為我不願意，而是因為我沒有時間。）

***Not that** I loved Caesar less, **but that** I loved Rome more.*

— *Shakespeare, Julius Caesar*

（並非我比較不愛凱撒，而是因為我更愛羅馬。）

本句可解釋為 I do not mean ***that** I loved Caesar less, **but that** I loved Rome more.* 的省略。

⑪ {
for the reason that
by reason that
on the ground(s) that
} （因為）

I don't like her *for the reason that she is a lazy girl.*

= I don't like her for the reason of her laziness.

（我不喜歡她，因為她是一個懶惰的女孩。）

He looks down on us ***by reason that** we are poor.*

= He looks down on us by reason of our being poor.

（因為我們貧窮，他看不起我們。）

He was dismissed ***on the ground***(*s*) ***that*** *he did not work hard.*

（他因為工作不努力而被解僱。）

【註】上述三種連接詞片語可通用，也可將 that 換成 of，簡化成片語介詞。

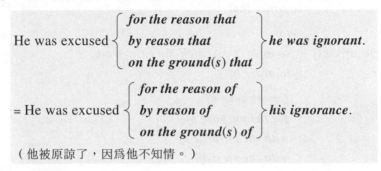

（他被原諒了，因為他不知情。）

6. 表目的的從屬連接詞：

(1) $\begin{cases} \textbf{that} \\ \textbf{so that} \\ \textbf{in order that} \end{cases}$ …**may (might)**（為了…；以便…）

Bring it nearer ***that I may*** *see it better.*（把它拿近一點，以使我看得比較清楚些。）

【主要子句為現在式或未來式時，that 子句用 may】

They died ***that we*** ***might*** *live.*（他們是為了我們的生存而死的。）

【主要子句為過去式時，that 子句用 might】

I will put it on the wall ***so that*** *everybody* ***may*** *look at it.*

（我要將它貼在牆上，以便每個人都可以看到它。）

He went to Japan ***so that*** *he* ***might*** *make a fortune there.*

（他到日本去，為了在那裡發財。）

He studies hard ***in order that*** *he* ***may*** *succeed.*（他為了要成功而努力用功。）

He rested ***in order that*** *he* ***might*** *work harder.*（他為了要更努力工作而休息。）

【註 1】that 子句中用 may (might) 比較正式，但現在也有人用 can, could, will, would。

　　　I'm giving my boy a good education ***so that*** *he* ***can*** *more easily cope with life's difficulties.*（我要給我的孩子良好的教育，以使他更能輕易地應付生活中的困難。）

　　　I studied the chapter ***so that I could*** *pass the examination.*
　　　（我研讀了這一章以便能通過考試。）

【註 2】that, so that, in order that 三者之中，只有 in order that 可放在句首。

　　　In order that *no man* ***might*** *enter*, *the servant locked the door.*
　　　（為了不使人進來，佣人把門鎖上。）

【註 3】除了註 2 的情形之外，其他的情形 that, so that, in order that 三者通用。當主要子句和副詞子句主詞相同時，可化爲表目的之不定詞片語和表目的之動名詞片語。

Betty got up early
$\begin{cases} \textbf{\textit{that}} \\ \textbf{\textit{so that}} \\ \textbf{\textit{in order that}} \end{cases}$
*she **might** catch the early train.*

= Betty got up early
$\begin{cases} \textbf{\textit{to}} \\ \textbf{\textit{so as to}} \\ \textbf{\textit{in order to}} \end{cases}$
***catch** the early train.*

= Betty got up early
$\begin{cases} \textbf{\textit{for the sake of}} \\ \textbf{\textit{for the purpose of}} \\ \textbf{\textit{with the purpose of}} \\ \textbf{\textit{with the view of}} \\ \textbf{\textit{with the aim of}} \\ \textbf{\textit{with the intention of}} \\ \textbf{\textit{with the object of}} \\ \textbf{\textit{with a view to}} \\ \textbf{\textit{with an eye to}} \end{cases}$
***catching** the early train.*

（爲了要趕早班火車，貝蒂起得很早。）

※ **for + 動名詞不可表目的；for + 名詞可表目的。**

Betty got up early *for catching the early train*.【誤】

Betty got up early *for the early train*.【正】

We went there *for sightseeing*.【正】【sightseeing 是名詞，參照 p.429】

（我們到那裡去觀光。）

【註 4】若主要子句的主詞和副詞子句的主詞不同時，可化成 for + 名詞 + 不定詞的形式。

He spoke very slowly
$\begin{cases} \textbf{\textit{that}} \\ \textbf{\textit{so that}} \\ \textbf{\textit{in order that}} \end{cases}$
*we **might** understand him*.【主詞不同】

= He spoke very slowly *for us to understand him*.

（他說得很慢，好讓我們了解他的話。）

【註 5】*to the end that*; *to the intent that*; *on purpose that*，也可視爲表「目的」的連接詞。

He did this *to the end that* he might carry off the first prize.

（他做這件事是爲了要得頭獎。）

(2)
$\begin{cases} \textbf{lest} \\ \textbf{for fear (that)} \\ \textbf{in case (that)} \end{cases}$
···**should + V**（以免；惟恐；以防；爲了不）：表否定目的。

（口語中可用直說法現在式代替 should + V，如第 5 例句）

I put away my pistol *lest he **should** touch it*.（我把手槍收起來，以免他去碰它。）

He locked up his money *lest it **should** be stolen*.（他把錢鎖好，以免被偷。）

She worried *for fear* (*that*) *the child would be hurt.*

（她擔心孩子會受傷。）

I cannot sleep at night *for fear* (*that*) *I should be attacked.*

（我晚上不敢睡，怕被攻擊。）

Better chain up the dog *in case* (*that*) *he bites.*

（最好把狗用鍊子拴住，以免牠咬人。）

【註1】 此類連接詞引導的子句通常用 should，但在美語中 lest 後的 should 可省略。

He hid it *lest she see it.*（他把它藏起來，以免被她看到。）

He will hide it *lest she see it.*（他將把它藏起來，以免會被她看到。）

Lest I forget, I'll write it down.
= I'll write it down *lest I should* forget.

（我要把它寫下來，以免會忘記。）

【註2】 此類子句中的 should 也可以用 shall, may, might 或 will 代替，但此種用法較不
普遍。

He is keeping quiet *for fear* (*that*) *he* $\begin{cases} \textbf{\textit{should}} \\ \textbf{\textit{shall}} \\ \textbf{\textit{may}} \\ \textbf{\textit{might}} \\ \textbf{\textit{will}} \end{cases}$ *disturb his father.*

（他正保持安靜，以免打擾他父親。）

【註3】 此類連接詞所引導的副詞子句可以換成 that, so that, in order that 接否定動詞。若
主要子句的主詞和副詞子句的主詞相同時，亦可化成表否定目的之不定詞片語和表
否定目的之動名詞片語。

Betty got up early $\begin{cases} \textbf{\textit{lest}} \\ \textbf{\textit{for fear}} \, (\textbf{\textit{that}}) \\ \textbf{\textit{in case}} \, (\textbf{\textit{that}}) \end{cases}$ *she should miss the early train.*

= Betty got up early $\begin{cases} \textbf{\textit{that}} \\ \textbf{\textit{so that}} \\ \textbf{\textit{in order that}} \end{cases}$ *she might not miss the early train.*

= Betty got up early $\begin{cases} \textbf{\textit{so as not to}} \\ \textbf{\textit{in order not to}} \end{cases}$ *miss the early train.*

= Betty got up early *for fear of missing the early train.*

（貝蒂起得很早，惟恐趕不上早班火車。）

7. **表結果的從屬連接詞：**

(1) **so…that**（如此…以致於）

that 引導副詞子句修飾前面的相關副詞 so，表前面原因的結果。**so 是副詞，後接形容詞、副詞或動詞。**

The bus was *so* full ***that*** *I could hardly turn around.*

（公車是如此的擁擠，致使我幾乎不能轉身。）

He was *so* clever ***that*** *he could not be defeated in argument.*

（他是如此聰明，以致於他的論點無法被人駁倒。）

Billy pitched *so* well ***that*** *everyone cheered him at the end of the game.*

（比利投得那麼好，以致於比賽結束時每個人都對他歡呼。）

He is *so* honest a man ***that*** *he will not accept a bribe.*（他是個誠實的人，不會收受賄賂。）

【爲了配合 so 的修飾，將 honest 放在冠詞 a 的前面，參閱 p.216】

It *so* happened ***that*** *he was not at home.*（他碰巧不在家。）

(2) **such…that**（如此…以致於）

that 引導副詞子句修飾前面的相關形容詞 such，表前面原因的結果。**such 是形容詞，後接名詞，或在 be 動詞後，做主詞補語。**

He was *such* a good runner ***that*** *I couldn't catch him.*

（他是一位這樣好的飛毛腿，以致於我無法捉到他。）

She spoke with *such* eloquence ***that*** *she moved the audience to tears.*

（她口才很好，以致於聽衆感動得掉眼淚。）

He had *such* a fright ***that*** *he fainted.*（他受到如此大的驚嚇，結果昏倒了。）

The force of the explosion was *such* ***that*** *all the windows were broken.*【such 做主詞補語】
$$\parallel$$
so great

= *Such* was the force of the explosion ***that*** *all the windows were broken.*

（爆炸的力量那麼大，以致於所有的窗戶都震破了。）

【註 1】 在口語中，或 **so**（*or* **such**）後字群不太長時，**that** 可以省略。

The orange was *so* sour (***that***) *I couldn't eat it.*（柳橙酸得我沒辦法吃。）

I am *so* sleepy (***that***) *I can't keep my eyes open.*（我愛睏得睜不開眼。）

It was *such* a lovely day (***that***) *everybody was feeling happy and cheerful.*

（那是一個令人愉快的一天，大家都感到快樂和高興。）

> We were in *such* a hurry (***that***) *we could not wait for our uncle to bring us from the* station.（我們很趕時間，以致於不能等待叔叔把我們從車站接來。）

> ※ **在口語中，甚至有時將 that 子句置於句首**，並省略 that。由含有 so 的主要子句來 說明。
>
> *I don't know what to do*, I feel *so* happy.（我高興得不知道做什麼好。）
>
> = I feel *so* happy ***that*** *I don't know what to do*.

【註 2】 such…that 句型中 that 所引導副詞子句省略，則 such 表示感嘆。

Don't be in *such* a hurry.（不要那麼匆忙。）

= *Don't be in* so great a hurry!

We had *such* a good time.（我們玩得很愉快。）

= What a good time *we had*!

【註 3】 such…that 和 such…as 的結構不同，that 為連接詞，引導副詞子句；as 為關係代名詞，

引導形容詞子句。（詳見 p.159）

$$\text{副　詞　子　句}$$

It is such a heavy stone ***that*** *he can't lift it.*

（那是一塊那麼重的石頭，以致於他抬不動它。）

$$\text{形　容　詞　子　句}$$

It is such a heavy stone ***as he can't lift.***（那是一塊他無法抬起的大石頭。）

【關代除了引導形容詞子句，在子句中還做 lift 的受詞】

【註 4】 **so…that 和 such…that 的比較**

① so 為副詞，後面可接動詞、形容詞、副詞；而 such 為形容詞，後面只可接名詞。

He is { *so* honest / *such* an honest man } that everybody trusts him.

【so 修飾 honest；such, an 和 honest 都是修飾 man 的形容詞】

（他是如此的誠實，以致於每個人都信任他。）

Man is *so* created ***that he lives with woman.***

（男人是造來和女人共同生活的。）【so 接動詞 created】

He spoke *so* rapidly ***that we could not clearly understand him.***

（他說話太快，以致於我們無法完全聽懂。）【so 接副詞 rapidly】

② **such + adj. +** { **不可數名詞** / **多數可數名詞** } **+ that** 的句型不可以用 so…that 代換。

so…that 只可用於 so + adj. + a + 單數可數名詞 + that 的情形。

It is { *such*【正】 / *so*【誤】 } nice weather ***that*** *I don't like to stay at home.*

（天氣那麼好，我不想待在家裡。）

They are $\left\{\begin{array}{l} \textbf{\textit{such}}【正】\\ \textit{so}【誤】 \end{array}\right\}$ good students ***that*** every teacher likes them.

（他們是那麼好的學生，以致於每位老師都喜歡他們。）

【註5】 表結果的副詞子句可改爲表結果的不定詞片語。

He is *so* honest ***that*** he will **not** accept a bribe.

= He is *too* honest ***to*** accept a bribe.

（他是那樣的誠實，不會收受賄賂。）【too…to 中的不定詞片語表否定的結果，參閱 p.415】

It was *so* cold last night ***that*** one could scarcely bear it.

= It was *so* cold last night ***as to*** be scarcely bearable.

（昨夜冷得幾乎令人無法忍受。）【as to 修飾副詞 so 表前面原因的結果】

He was *so* insolent ***that*** he disobeyed his master.

= He was insolent *enough* ***to*** disobey his master.

（他非常無禮，不服從他的主人。）【enough to 中的不定詞片語表肯定的結果】

⑶ **so (that)** （所以）【現代美語常用 so 來代替 so that，表結果】

He worked very hard, ***so (that)*** he became rich in a very short time.

（他非常努力工作，所以不久就致富了。）

Nothing more was heard of him, ***so (that)*** people thought that he was dead.

（沒有聽到他的消息，所以人們認爲他死了。）

It rained hard ***so (that)*** I didn't bother to water the lawn.

（下了大雨，所以我不必費心去替草坪澆水了。）

【註】 so (that) 可引導表目的的子句，又可引導表結果的子句。表結果的 so that 之前有時加
逗點（,），表目的通常有 may (might)，但表結果有時又有 may，所以區別時，須理解
前後文的關係才行。見下面兩例：

He spoke clearly, ***so that*** everyone could hear. 【表結果】
（他說得很清楚，所以每個人都聽到了。）
He spoke clearly, ***so that*** everyone might hear. 【表目的】
（他說得很清楚，以便每個人都能聽到。）

John slammed the door ***so that*** he awakened his mother. 【表結果】
（約翰用力關門，所以把他母親吵醒了。）
John slammed the door ***so that*** his mother would know he was home. 【表目的】
（約翰用力關門，以便於讓他母親知道他回家了。）

(4) $\left\{\begin{array}{l}\textbf{but}\\ \textbf{but that}\\ \textbf{but what}\end{array}\right\}$（而不）

在否定的表達後，特別是否定的 so 和 such 之後，可用 but (that) 或 but what 引導表示結果的副詞子句，**構成前後的雙重否定**，可譯成「沒有…不」。此時 but 或 but that 可作 "that…not 或 unless" 解。

It never rains *but it pours*.（不雨則已，一雨傾盆；禍不單行。）

= It never rains *unless it pours*.

He is not *so* sick *but he can eat*.（他並未病到不能吃東西的程度。）

= He is not *so* sick *that he* can*not* eat.

He is not *so* old *but that* he can walk.（他並未老到不能走路。）

= He is not *so* old *that he can not* walk.

= He is not too old to walk.

I never see you *but I think of my brother*.（每次見到你，我就會想起我哥哥。）

He never fought *but he won*.（他從來沒有打架而不贏的。）

There is no man so friendless *but what he can find a friend sincere enough to tell him a disagreeable truth*.（再孤立的人都可找到一位真摯的朋友，來傾訴令人不愉快的事實。）

He is not *such* a fool *but that he knows it*.（他並非笨得不知此事。）

> 【註】**but** 的其他用法：
>
> ① *but* (*that*) 還可以引導名詞子句。（參閱 p.24, 486）
> ② *but* 在否定表達後，還可當關係代名詞，引導形容詞子句。（參閱 p.160）
> ③ *but that* 還可引導表條件的副詞子句，當「如果不是因為」解。（參閱 p.522）
> ④ *never…but* 還可以做對等連接詞。（參閱 p.470）

8. **表條件的從屬連接詞**：關於條件子句的詳細用法，可參閱 p.361「假設法」。

⑴ **if**（如果；假如）

He would have signed the contract *if it had been satisfactory*.

（如果合約令人滿意的話，他早就簽了。）

If it is fine next Saturday, we shall have a party.

（如果下星期六天氣很好，我們將舉辦宴會。）

If I had a car, I should go there at once.（如果我有車，我會立刻到那裡去。）

> 【註 1】**if** 還可以作 **when** 或 **whenever** 解。
>
> *If water boils*, it changes into steam.（水煮沸就變成蒸氣。）
>
> = *When* water boils, it changes into steam.

If she wants the servant, she rings the bell. (她需要佣人的時候就會按鈴。)
= *Whenever she wants the servant*, she rings the bell.

【註2】 **if** 有時還可以作 **although** (雖然) 解。(詳見 p.524)

If he is old, he is strong. (他雖然老，但他很強壯。)
= *Although he is old*, he is strong.

(2) **unless** (除非；如果不) (是 if…not 的加強語氣)

The baby will never cry *unless he is hungry*. (除非那嬰兒餓了，不然他絕不會哭。)

You will not pass the examination, *unless you study hard*.
(除非你努力用功，不然你不會通過考試。)

George never speaks *unless (he is) spoken to*.
(除非有人對喬治說話，否則他絕不會講話。)
【if 和 unless 後，主詞和 be 動詞在句意明確時可省略】

Unless (I am) compelled to stay in by bad weather, I go for a walk every day.
(除非惡劣的天氣迫使我留在家裡，我每天都會出去散步。)

(3) { **as long as** / **so long as** } (= **if only**) (只要)

You may borrow this book *as long as you keep it clean*.
(只要你保持這本書清潔，你就可以借它。)

I will go *as long as he asks me*. (只要他要我去，我就會去。)

You may stay here *so long as you keep quiet*.
(只要你保持安靜，你就可以待在這裡。)

I can do it *so long as you give me time*. (只要你給我時間，我就能做它。)

Anything will do, *so long as it is interesting*. (只要有趣，任何事都可以。)

You may take it home *so long as you pay for it*.
(只要你付錢，你就可以把它帶回家。)

(4) **in case** (= **if**) (如果)：in case 後從前常加 that，但現在不加。

In case I forget, please remind me of my promise. (假如我忘掉，請你提醒我所做的承諾。)
【in case 也可引導表否定目的的副詞子句，參閱 p.514】

He will do the work *in case you pay the money*. (假如你付錢，他就會做那件工作。)

You may call this number *in case I am not home*. (如果我不在家，你可以打這個電話號碼。)

【註】
$$\left\{\begin{array}{l} \textit{in case} + 子句 \\ \textit{in case of} + 名詞 \\ \textit{in the case of} + 名詞（= as regards）（關於；就…而論） \end{array}\right.$$（如果；萬一）

副詞┌子句┐
***In case** it rains*, don't expect me.（萬一下雨了，就不必等我了。）

副詞┌片語┐
= ***In case** of rain*, don't expect me.

副詞┌片語┐
***In the case of** rain*, we don't have much rain in autumn and winter in the central part of Taiwan.（就雨量而言，台灣中部在秋冬兩季少雨。）

⑸ **if only**（只要）

***If** he can **only** get a chance*, he will be able to do great service.

（只要他有機會，他就能夠提供很棒的服務。）

This boy is very clever, and ***if** he can **only** be well-educated*, he will become a scholar.

（這男孩非常聰明，只要能接受良好的敎育，就可成爲學者。）

I'll let you use the bicycle ***if only** you keep it in good condition*.

（只要你把腳踏車保養好，我就讓你使用它。）

***If** you **only** read this book carefully*, you will be good at English.

（只要你仔細地讀這本書，你就會精通英文。）

【註】if only 用於直說法的感嘆句，表示說話者認爲可能實現的願望。

***If only** he arrives in time!*（他要是能及時到達就好了！）

※ if only 還可用於假設法，表示願望。（詳見 p.370）

⑹ **only if**（只有）

I told him he could succeed ***only if** he tried hard.*（我告訴他，只有努力才能成功。）

***Only if** it is nice out* can the athletic meeting be held.

（只有天氣好，運動會才能舉行。）【only 放在句首時，主要子句須倒裝】

⑺ **on condition (that)**（只要；如果）

I will pardon him ***on condition (that)** he acknowledges his fault.*
（如果他認錯，我就會原諒他。）

You can go swimming ***on condition (that)** you don't go too far from the river bank.*
（只要你不離河岸太遠，你就可以去游泳。）

You may borrow this book ***on condition (that)** you return it tomorrow.*
（只要你明天歸還這本書，就可以借你。）

(8)
$$\left.\begin{array}{l} \textbf{suppose (that)} \\ \textbf{supposing (that)} \\ \textbf{provided (that)} \\ \textbf{providing (that)} \end{array}\right\} \text{(= if)（如果）}$$

Suppose (*that*) *I were to help you*, would you try it again?
（如果我幫助你，你願不願再試一次？）【suppose 較 suppose that 常用】

Suppose I were a bird, I would fly to you. （如果我是隻鳥，我會飛到你身邊。）

Suppose I meet him, what shall I tell him? （如果我遇見了他，我該告訴他什麼呢？）

Supposing (*that*) *you died*, what would become of your children?
（如果你死了，你的孩子會變成怎麼樣呢？）

Supposing (*that*) *it rains tomorrow*, what shall we do?
（如果明天下雨了，我們怎麼辦？）

We shall start at three o'clock *provided* (*that*) *the car is ready then*.
（如果車子在那時準備妥當，我們將在三點啟程。）

I don't mind lending you the money *provided* (*that*) *you pay it back within a year*.
（如果你在一年之內還我，我不介意把錢借你。）

I will come *providing* (*that*) *I have time*. （如果有時間，我會來的。）

I will go *providing my expenses are paid*. （如果我的開銷有人付，我就去。）
【providing 較 providing that 常用】

He will go *providing it doesn't rain*. （如果不下雨，他就會去。）

【註】 *say* 也可以代替 *suppose*。

Suppose you were in his place, would you do it?
= *Say you were in his place*, would you do it?
（假如你站在他的立場，你會做那件事嗎？）

(9) **but that** (= only that)（**如果不是因為**）

I should have started *but that the weather was so bad*.
‖
had it not been for the fact that
（如果不是天氣那麼糟，我早就出發了。）

But that you aided me, I should have failed.
= *If you had not aided me*, I should have failed.
（若非你幫助我，我早就失敗了。）

I would go abroad, ***but that*** *I am so poor.*（若非那麼貧窮，我就出國了。）

= I would go abroad *if I were not so poor.*

But that *he is in debt*, he would leave this country.

（他如果沒負債，他就會離開這個國家。）

　【註】***but that***, ***but for***, ***except that***, ***except for*** 的區別，請參閱 p.366。

⑽ **so that**（= **so long as**）（只要）

You may keep the toy as long as you like, ***so that*** *you bring it back in good condition.*

（這玩具你願意玩多久就玩多久，只要你將它完好地歸還就行了。）

So that *it be done*, I don't care who does it.（只要能完成，我不在乎由誰去做。）

You can stay as long as you like ***so that*** *you catch the train.*

（只要能趕上火車，你要留多久就留多久。）

　【註】***so that*** 還可以引導表目的和結果的副詞子句。（參閱 p.513, 518）

⑾ **once**（= **if you**…; **as soon as**）（一旦）

Once *you understand this rule*, you will have no further difficulty.

（一旦你了解這個規則，就不會再有困難。）

You cannot get out, ***once*** *you are in.*（你一旦進去了，你就出不來。）

Once *you hear the story*, you will never be able to forget it.

（一旦你聽了這故事，就永遠無法忘記。）

Once *(it is) seen*, the picture can never be forgotten.

（一旦那幅畫被看見了，就永遠無法被忘懷。）

【當 once 所引導的副詞子句主詞與主要子句的主詞相同時或句意明確時，once 後的主詞和 be 動詞可省略】

⑿ **where**…**there**（若…則…）

Where *there is a will* **there** is a way.
　‖
　If

（如果你有意志力，一定會找到一個方法。—— 有志者事竟成。）

Where *there is no fire*, **there** is no smoke.

（沒有火就不會有煙。—— 無風不起浪。）

Where *your treasure is*, **there** will your heart also be.

（你的財寶在哪裡，你的心就在那裡。）

Where *there is no rain*, **there** is no farming.（沒有雨的地方，就沒有農業。）

⒀ **in the event that** (= **in case**; **if**)（如果；萬一；一旦）

In the event that our team wins, there will be a big celebration.

〔一旦（如果）我隊獲勝，就會有一個盛大的慶祝活動。〕

What will you do *in the event that you fail again*?（萬一你又失敗了，你將怎麼辦？）

【註】若用片語介詞 *in the event of* 則須接名詞當受詞。

In the event that it rains, I will not go.（如果下雨了，我就不去。）
= *In the event of rain*, I will not go.
= *In case it rains*, I will not go.
= *In case of rain*, I will not go.

⒁ **only that** (= **were it not that**)（如果不是；只是）

I would come, *only that I am engaged to dine out*.

（如果不是跟人約好要出外用餐，我就會來。）【主要子句為假設法時 only that = but that】

He would probably do well in the examination, *only that he gets rather nervous*.

（如果不是他相當緊張，他可能會考得很好。）

He is a good student, *only that he is a little lazy*.

（他是個好學生，只是他有點懶惰。）【主要子句為直說法時 only that = except that】

【註】*only that* 為表條件的從屬連接詞，而 *only* 可當反義對等連接詞等於 *but*，兩者不可混淆。(參閱 p.471)

9. **表讓步的從屬連接詞：**表讓步就是對主要子句所說的話在語氣上加以退讓，通常作「雖然；即使；無論；儘管」解。

⑴ **if**（雖然；即使）：語氣沒有 even if 或 even though 的強。

I'll do it, *if it takes me all afternoon*.（即使這件工作會用去我整個下午，我也要做。）

If he is little, he is strong.（他雖然小，但卻很強壯。）

I'll do it *if I die in the attempt*!（即使我嘗試做這件事會喪命，我仍然要做！）

⑵ **whether…or**（無論）【or 不可省略】

I will go *whether it rains or shines*.（無論晴雨我都要去。）

Whether we win or lose, we are going to do our best.

（無論是勝是敗，我們都會盡最大的努力。）

Whether you like it or not, you will have to do it.

（無論你是不是喜歡，你一定要做。）

Whether *you go **or** stay*, you must pay a week's board.

（無論你去或留，你都必須付一週的伙食費。）

Whether *it rains **or** not*, I will go swimming.

（無論晴雨，我都要去游泳。）

Whether (*he is*) *waking **or** sleeping*, he breathes noisily.

（不論是醒著或是睡著，他呼吸總是很大聲。）

【whether 後的主詞和主要子句的主詞相同時，whether 後的主詞和 be 動詞可省略】

> 【註】 *whether*…(***or not***) 也可以引導名詞子句，但 or not 可省略。（參閱 p.484）

> I wonder ***whether*** *he will come* (***or not***). （我不知道他會不會來。）

(3) **notwithstanding** (**that**) (= **though, although**)（ **雖然** ）

Notwithstanding (***that***) *he works very hard*, he can't support his family.

（雖然他工作很努力，他卻無法維持家計。）

He is not contented ***notwithstanding*** (***that***) *he is so rich*.

（雖然他是那麼有錢，他還不滿足。）

Notwithstanding (***that***) *there was need for haste*, he still delayed.

（雖然必須要趕快，他仍然在拖延。）

(4) **when** (= **though, although**)（ **雖然** ）

She bought two coats ***when*** *she needed but one*.

（雖然她只需要一件外套，可是她買了兩件。）

We have only three books ***when*** *we need five*.

（雖然我們需要五本書，我們卻只有三本。）

She stopped trying, ***when*** *she might have succeeded next time*.

（雖然她下次可能成功，她卻停止嘗試了。）

(5) **(al)though**（ **雖然** ）

Though *I have known Mr. Smith for thirty years*, I have never addressed him by his first name. （雖然我認識史密斯先生已有三十年，但我從來沒有直呼其名過。）

Although *all men were against him*, he none the less persevered.

（雖然眾人都反對他，他仍然堅持到底。）

Although *the enemy resisted stubbornly*, our army occupied the town according to the original schedule. （敵人雖然頑固地抵抗，我們的陸軍還是按照原來的計畫佔領了那城鎮。）

Though he has denied the deed, no one will believe his word.
（雖然他已否認這個行為，但沒有人會相信他的話。）

Though (*he was*) *very tired*, he did not give up. （雖然很疲倦，但他並沒有放棄。）

【though 後的主詞和主要子句的主詞相同時，though 後的主詞和 be 動詞可省略】

【註 1】 *though* 所引導的副詞子句置於主要子句前後皆可，當其置於主要子句之前時，在主要子句之前端可加 *still*, *yet* 或 *nevertheless* 來加強語氣。

> I will trust in him *though* he punishes me. （雖然他處罰我，我仍信任他。）
> *Though* he punishes me, **yet** I will trust in him.

> He is not vain *though* he is learned. （雖然他很博學，但他不自負。）
> *Though* he is learned, **nevertheless** he is not vain.

【註 2】 中文有「雖然…但是…」的句型，而英文中兩個子句只能用一個連接詞，所以 (*al*)*though* 或 *but* 只能擇其一，不能同時使用。

> *Although* I believe it, (**yet**) I will not act now. 【正】
> I believe it, **but** I will not act now. 【正】
> *Although* I believe it, *but* I will not act now. 【誤】
> （雖然我相信它，我現在卻不願有所行動。）

⑹ > **even though** > （即使；雖然）
> **even if**

I would not do such a thing, *even though* I were to get a million dollars.
（即使我能得一百萬元，我也不會做這種事。）

My grades were always excellent, *even though* I was often absent.
（我雖然時常缺席，但我的成績卻一直很好。）

She won't leave the television set, *even though* her husband is waiting for his supper.
（雖然她的丈夫等著她吃晚飯，她還是不肯離開電視。）

Even though he affirmed it, I would not believe it.
（即使他確認那件事，我還是不相信。）

Even if I were starving, I would not ask a favor of him.
（即使我要餓死，也不會請他幫忙。）

Even if my watch is right, we shall be late. （即使我的錶正確，我們也會遲到。）

【註】 *even if* 與 *even though* 所引導的副詞子句中的動詞，用直說法或用假設法的意義就有所不同。（詳見 p.367）

> *Even if* I were busy, I would go. 【假設法】
> （即使我忙，我也要去。—— 事實上我現在並不忙）
> *Even if* I am busy, I will go. 【直說法】
> （雖然我忙，我也要去。—— 我現在的確很忙）

(7) $\left\{\begin{array}{l}\textbf{no matter} + 疑問詞 \\ 疑問詞\textbf{-ever}\end{array}\right\}$ + **may**（無論…）【用不用 may 均可】

> *whoever*, *whichever*, *whatever* 三者具有名詞的性質，故在子句之中須當主詞或受詞。
> *whichever*, *whatever* 還具有形容詞的性質，可修飾名詞。（參照 p.158）
> *whenever*, *wherever*, *however* 三者具有副詞性質，修飾子句中的動詞、形容詞或副詞。
> （參照 p.245）

No matter who
Whoever } *comes* (or *may come*), he will be welcome.（無論誰來都會受到歡迎。）

No matter whom
Whomever } *you* (*may*) *doubt*, never doubt yourself.

（無論你懷疑誰，絕不能懷疑自己。）

No matter which
Whichever } *you* (*may*) *choose*, you will be pleased.

（無論你選哪一個，你都會滿意。）

No matter what
Whatever } *you* (*may*) *do*, do it well.（無論你做什麼，都要好好地做。）

No matter when
Whenever } *my mother goes* (or *may go*) *shopping*, she takes me with her, and

makes me carry all she buys.

（我媽媽無論什麼時候去買東西，她總是把我帶在身邊，叫我提她所買的東西。）

No matter where
Wherever } *you* (*may*) *live*, you cannot be happy without a friend.

（無論你住在什麼地方，沒有朋友就不可能快樂。）

No matter how
However } *little ability a man has* (or *may have*), it is not impossible for him to

do something if he be but diligent.

（無論一個人的能力多麼小，只要勤勉，要有所成就並非不可能。）

【註 1】 *whether* 和 *if* 也可接在 *no matter* 之後。

　　　Mary wanted to get to school on time, *no matter if she went without breakfast*.

　　　（瑪麗想要準時到校，不論她是不是吃了早餐。）

　　　No matter whether it will rain or not, we have decided to leave at six in the
　　　　morning.

　　　（不管是不是會下雨，我們已決定在早上六點離開。）

【註2】 *whatever*, *however* 所引導的表讓步副詞子句句意明確時，省略 *may* (*might*) *be*，副詞子句的主詞和動詞和主要子句相同時，也可一併省略。

Whatever his age (*might be*), Johnny Wood never seemed to grow up.
（無論強尼・伍德的年齡多大，他似乎永遠長不大。）

However imperfect our machines (*may be*), they can help us amazingly.
（我們的機器無論多麼不完美，卻能對我們大有幫助。）

Any government, *however* constituted (*it may be*), must respect the people's wishes. （任何政府無論其組織如何，都必須尊重人民的意願。）

【註3】 *whoever*, *whomever*, *whichever*, *whatever* 也可引導名詞子句。（詳見 p.24, 158）

(8) { while / whereas } （雖然；即使）

whereas 語氣比 while 較強。while 用於表時間的副詞子句較普遍，引導表讓步的副詞子句較少，究竟 while 表時間或表讓步，要看句意而定。

While I admit that the problems are difficult, I don't agree that they cannot be solved.
（雖然我承認這些問題很困難，我並不同意它們無法解決。）

While I like the color of the hat, I do not like its shape.
（雖然我喜歡這頂帽子的顏色，可是不喜歡它的形狀。）

While this is true of some, it is not true of all.
（雖然這適用於一些情況，但並非適用於全部。）

While I believe he is honest, I suspect his memory.
（雖然我相信他是誠實的，但卻懷疑他的記憶力。）

Misers mistake gold for good, *whereas* it is only a means of obtaining it.
（金子雖然只是獲得幸福的一種方法，但守財奴卻誤認為金子就是幸福。）

Whereas three years ago this country stood third in the list of exporting countries, today she stands first.
（雖然三年前我國在輸出國家中排名第三，現在卻排名第一。）

【註】 *while* 和 *whereas* 還可當反義對等連接詞，請參閱 p.471；*while* 還可引導表時間的副詞子句，請參閱 p.490。

Some have nothing to eat, *while* others eat too much.
對等連接詞
（有些人沒有東西吃，而有些人則是吃得太多。）

Some girls like the so-called miniskirt, *whereas* others dislike it.
對等連接詞
（有些女孩子喜歡所謂的迷你裙，而有些則不喜歡。）

⑼ **as**（= **though**, **although**）（雖然）

as 用於表讓步的副詞子句，有下列幾種形式：

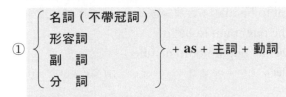

① 名詞（不帶冠詞）/ 形容詞 / 副詞 / 分詞 ⎱ + **as** + 主詞 + 動詞

*Child **as** he is*, he can answer the question.

= *Although he is a child*, he can answer the question.

（他雖然是個小孩，卻能回答這個問題。）

*Poor **as** he was*, he was above selling his honor at any price.

= *Though he was poor*, he was above selling his honor at any price.

（他雖然貧窮，卻不屑於出賣他的名譽。）

*Rashly **as** he acted*, he had some excuse.

= *Although he acted rashly*, he had some excuse.

（雖然他的行為粗魯，卻是有理由的。）

*Surrounded **as** he was by the enemy*, he was not afraid.

= *Though he was surrounded by the enemy*, he was not afraid.

（雖然他受敵人包圍，他並不害怕。）

② 動詞 + **as** + 主詞 + 助動詞

*Detest him **as** we may*, we must acknowledge his greatness.

= *No matter how we may detest him*, we must acknowledge his greatness.

（無論我們如何討厭他，也不能不承認他的偉大。）

*Try **as** he may*, he never seems able to do the work satisfactorily.

= *Though he tries hard*, he never seems able to do the work satisfactorily.

（雖然他很努力，卻似乎無法把這工作做得很令人滿意。）

*Try **as** I would*, I couldn't open it.（無論我怎麼試，都打不開它。）

= *However hard I might try*, I couldn't open it.

【註 1】 *though* 和 *that* 也可代替 *as* 用於上述句型中，但 *although* 不行。

　　　Rich ⎱ *though*【正】/ *although*【誤】 ⎰ *he is*, he is not happy.（他雖然富有，卻不快樂。）

　　　= *Rich **as** he is*, he is not happy.

　　　*Strong man **that**（= **as**）he is*, General Botha has been severely put to the test
　　　　during the past few weeks.

　　　（波塔將軍雖然堅強，在過去的數週裡，也受到了嚴重的考驗。）

【註 2】 Be + 主詞 + 形容詞，或命令動詞 + 疑問詞 + 主詞 + 助動詞等沒有連接詞的句型，也可表示讓步。(參閱 p.360 ⑵)

Be a man ever so rich, he ought not to be idle. (人無論多麼富有，都不該懶惰。)

= *Let a man be as rich as he will*, he ought not to be idle.

= *No matter how rich a man may be*, he ought not to be idle.

【be 是古代假設語氣的遺留，現在多用 let + 主詞 + be 表讓步。ever so 也可寫作 never so，並無否定之意，意思等於 "very"】

Call when you will, you will find her in her study.

= *No matter when you may call*, you will find her in her study.

(無論你何時去拜訪，你會發現她總是在書房裡。)

I shall have to buy the coat, *cost what it may*.

= I shall have to buy the coat, *no matter what it may cost*.

(無論須花費多少，我非買這件外套不可。)

【註 3】 上述 as 的句型可依句意表讓步或原因。比較下面兩句：

Hero as he was, he cried at the news. 【表讓步】

(他雖是一個英雄，聽到這消息也禁不住大哭。)

Hero as he was, he did not cry at the news. 【表原因】

(因爲他是英雄，所以聽到這消息並沒有哭。)

【註 4】 「現在 (過去) 分詞 + as one does (is) + 主要子句」的句型中 as one does (is) 很像是表讓步的副詞子句，但其實是當作加強語氣用的副詞子句，可能表原因，亦可能表讓步，視句意而定。as one does (is) 是插入語，其前後之逗點可省略。

Living, *as I do*, so remote from town, I rarely have visitors.
        ‖
       live

= *As I live so remote from town*, I rarely have visitors.

(我住得離城鎮如此的遙遠，所以很少有訪客。)

Tired, *as I was*, with my homework, I didn't enjoy the evening.

(我因爲做家庭作業而覺得累，所以那個晚上我過得並不快樂。)

【Tired 爲 Being tired 的省略】

Standing, *as it does*, on the top of the hill, the school commands a fine view.
        ‖
       stands

(因爲這所學校位於山頂上，所以能俯瞰一片美景。)

⑽ **for all (that)** (儘管；雖然)【that 常省略】

For all (that) he seems to dislike me, I still like him.

(雖然他好像不喜歡我，但我仍然喜歡他。)

For all (that) he is wealthy, he is not content. (他雖然富有，卻不滿足。)

【註1】此類表讓步的副詞子句可簡化成副詞片語。*for all* 可接子句或名詞（片語）爲受詞，*with all* 只能接名詞（片語）當受詞，不可接子句。

For all (*that*) *he is wealthy*, he is not happy.

$=\begin{cases} \textbf{\textit{For all}} \\ \textbf{\textit{With all}} \\ \textbf{\textit{In spite of}} \end{cases}$ *his wealth*, he is not happy.

= *Although he is wealthy*, he is not happy.

（雖然他很有錢，但他並不快樂。）

【註2】for all 中 **for** 是介系詞相當於 **in spite of**，**all** 可當代名詞或形容詞，all 當代名詞時，可接形容詞子句，也可接名詞子句，**只有在 all（代名詞）後接名詞子句做 all 的同位語時**，文法家爲了簡化，才把 for all (that) 看成連接詞引導表讓步的副詞子句。

介詞片語當副詞用

For all (*that*) *you say*, I still like her. （儘管你這麼說，我仍然喜歡她。）
代名詞　形容詞子句

= *In spite of* all (*that*) *you say*, I still like her.

代名　本來是名詞子句做 all 的同位語

For all (*that*) *he is wealthy*, he is not content. （他雖然富有，但不滿足。）
連接詞

For all his wealth, he was not happy. （他雖然有錢，但不快樂。）
形容詞

You will not be much better *for all* the books you read.
形容詞　　　名詞片語

（儘管你讀了這些書，你也好不了多少。）

He says he is innocent, but I'm sure he is guilty, *for all* that.
形容詞 代名

（他說他是無辜的，儘管如此，我還是相信他有罪。）

(11) $\begin{cases} \textbf{granting (that)} \\ \textbf{granted (that)} \\ \textbf{grant that} \\ \textbf{(while) admitting (that)} \\ \textbf{assuming (that)} \end{cases}$ （即使）

Granting (*that*) *it is true*, it does not concern me. （即使它是眞的，也與我無關。）

Granted (*that*) *this is true*, you are still in the wrong. （即使這是眞的，你還是錯。）

Admitting that he is very clever, he can't succeed without patience.

（即使他很聰明，但如果沒有耐心，也不會成功。）

Admitting that he has the ability to do that, he has to work hard to carry it out.
（即使他有能力做那件事，他仍須努力去完成。）

Assuming that it is so, you ought to have told her the truth.
（即使事情如此，你也應該對她說實話。）

【註】表讓步的各種句型大多可以代換。

> *(Al)though he is wealthy*, he is not content.（雖然他很富有，但並不滿足。）
> = *Wealthy as* (or *though*) *he is*, he is not content.

$$= \left\{\begin{array}{l} \textit{No matter how} \\ \textit{However} \\ \textit{Regardless of how} \end{array}\right\} \textit{wealthy he is}, \text{he is not content.}$$

$$= \left\{\begin{array}{l} \textit{Be he} \\ \textit{Let him be} \end{array}\right\} \textit{ever so wealthy}, \text{he is not content.}$$

> = *He is wealthy*, *but* he is not content.

$$= \left\{\begin{array}{l} \textit{Notwithstanding} \\ \textit{For all} \end{array}\right\} \textit{(that) he is wealthy}, \text{he is not content.}$$

$$= \left\{\begin{array}{l} \textit{Notwithstanding} \\ \textit{For all} \\ \textit{With all} \\ \textit{In spite of} \\ \textit{Despite} \\ \textit{After all} \end{array}\right\} \textit{his wealth}, \text{he is not content.}$$

$$= \left\{\begin{array}{l} \textit{In spite of the fact that} \\ \textit{Despite the fact that} \end{array}\right\} \textit{he is wealthy}, \text{he is not content.}$$

【注意】*despite*（介）和 *in spite of* 同義，但語氣較弱；在有些字典上仍可看見的 *despite of* 和 *in despite of* 現在已不通行，應該避免使用。

$$(12) \left\{\begin{array}{l} \textbf{not but} \\ \textbf{not but that} \\ \textbf{not but what} \end{array}\right\} （雖然；並非不；然而）$$

I can't come, *not but that I'd like to*.（雖然我想來，但是我不能來。）
= I can't come, *though I'd like to*.

$$\text{I can't help her}, \left\{\begin{array}{l} \textit{not but} \\ \textit{not but that} \\ \textit{not but what} \end{array}\right\} \textit{I pity her}. （雖然我很可憐她，但我不能幫助她。）$$

= I can't help her, *though I do pity her*.

【註】*but*, *but that*, *but what* 可以引導名詞子句（參照 p.486），也可引導表示結果的副詞子句（參照 p.519）。

IV. 綜合説明 *as*, *that*, *but*, *than* 的用法

1. *as* 的用法

⑴ 做從屬連接詞，引導副詞子句。

① 引導表「時間」的副詞子句，相當於 when 或 while。(詳見 p.490)

She sang ***as she worked***. (她一邊工作一邊唱歌。)

② 引導表「狀態」的副詞子句，相當於 in the same way that，作「像；依照」解。
(詳見 p.499)

He did ***as he was told***. (他按照指示做了。)

③ 引導表「原因」的副詞子句，相當於 since。(詳見 p.507)

As he was a friend of mine, I went to help him.
(因爲他是我的朋友，所以我去幫助他了。)

④ 引導表「讓步」的副詞子句，相當於 (al)though。(詳見 p.529)

Tired as he was, he sat up late studying last night.
(他雖然疲倦，昨夜還是讀書讀到很晚。)

⑤ 引導表「比較」的副詞子句。(詳見 p.506, 200)

You are as good ***as you think you are***. (你正如你自己所想像的那樣好。)

⑵ 做準關係代名詞，引導形容詞子句。(詳見 p.25, 159, 489)

She is looking for the same buttons ***as her mother wants***.

(她在找像她媽媽所要的那種鈕扣。)

⑶ 作指示副詞用。(詳見 p.506)

"**as**…as" 中的第一個 as 即指示副詞，修飾它後面的形容詞或副詞。

He is ***as*** tall as I (am). (他和我一樣高。)
　　指示副詞　連接詞

⑷ 作介詞用，作「擔任；充任」解。

Who will act ***as*** teacher? (誰將擔任老師？)

The actor who appeared ***as*** Romeo was his good friend.
(扮演羅密歐的演員，是他的好朋友。)

【註】as 後有時接（代）名詞或形容詞，看起來像是介系詞，事實上是一個省略句。
　　　(詳見 p.500)
　　　I regard him ***as*** my benefactor. (我當他是我的恩人。)
　　　= I regard him ***as if he were*** my benefactor.

⑸ **含有 as 的重要慣用語：**

① *as a matter of fact* (= really; actually) (事實上)

　　As a matter of fact, I was too late for the train. (事實上，我沒趕上火車。)

② *as a rule* (= generally) (通常；照例)

　　He comes on Monday *as a rule*. (他通常星期一來。)

③ *as against* (= in comparison with) (則…；比…；對…)

　　The business done this year amounts to ten thousand dollars *as against* eight thousand

　　　dollars last year. (今年營業總額爲一萬元，去年則爲八千元。)

④ *as concerning* (= as touching) (關於)

　　As concerning their retirement allowance, they are rather anxious about it.

　　(關於他們的退休金，他們是很擔心的。)

⑤ *as far as* (…至某地；就…所)

　　He walked *as far as* the station. (他走到車站去。)

　　= He walked to the station.

　　As far as I know, he is honest. (就我所知，他是誠實的。)

⑥ *as far as…is concerned* (關於；至於；就…而言)

　　As far as they themselves *are concerned*, they are safe and sound.

　　(至於他們自身，則安然無恙。)

⑦ *as follows* (= as comes next) (如下) (詳見 p.500)

　　Their names are *as follows*. (他們的名字如下。)

⑧ *as from* (= considered formally as dating from) 〔自 (…之日) 起〕

　　You've been hired *as from* last Sunday. (從上星期日起你已被正式僱用了。)

⑨ *as good as* (= the same thing as) (像…一樣；幾乎等於)

　　Will he be *as good as* his word? (他是否言而有信？)

　　He is *as good as* dead. (他就像死了一樣。)

　　= He is almost dead.

⑩ *as if* (= as though) (好像)

　　是表狀態的從屬片語連接詞。(詳見 p.371, 503)

　　He talks *as if he were a scholar*. (他說話的態度好像一位學者一般。)

⑪ *as it is*

　　✓ 用在句首時，作「事實上」(= as a matter of fact) 解。過去式爲 as it was。

　　　If I were a college graduate, I would go abroad. *As it is*, I cannot go.

　　　(如果我是大學畢業生，我就會出國。但事實上，我不能去。)

⒉ 用在句尾時，作「照原來的樣子」（= in its present condition）解。注意 as 子句的動詞。

The painter does not copy nature *as it is*.（畫家描繪大自然並不是完全寫實的。）

Paint *as it was*.（照它以前的樣子畫。）

You had better take things *as they are*.（你最好接受事物的現況。）

⑫ *as it were*（= so to speak）（好像）

He became, *as it were*, a kind of hero from a strange land.

（他好像變成了一個來自異鄉的英雄。）

⑬
- *as likely as not*（= with greater probability）（多半）【加強 likely 的語氣】
- *as often as not*（= very frequently）（常常）【加強 often（時常）的語氣】
- *as soon as not*（= more willingly）（寧願）【加強 soon（= rather）的語氣】

He will succeed *as likely as not*.（他多半會成功。）

During foggy weather the trains are late *as often as not*.

（有霧時火車常常誤點。）

I will stay at home *as soon as not*.（我寧願留在家裡。）

⑭ *as*（*or so*）*long as*

⒈ 在…的時候（= while）（詳見 p.494）

You shall never enter the house *as long as I live in it*.

（在我住在這裡的時候，你永遠不許進入這房子。）

⒉ 只要（= on condition that）（詳見 p.521）

You can go anywhere you like, *so long as* you get back before dark.

（你可以隨意到哪裡去，只要你在天黑以前回來。）

⑮ *as much as to say*（好像是說）

You said "all right" which was *as much as to say* that you were satisfied.

（你說「好」就好像是說你很滿意。）

⑯ *as one*（*man*）（一致地）

The country rose *as one*（*man*）against the invaders.

（全國一致團結起來抵抗入侵者。）

⑰ *as regards*（= as concerns）（至於）（詳見 p.500）

Now, *as regards* money, what is to be done?（那麼至於錢的問題，該怎麼辦？）

⑱ *as such*（= in that capacity）（作爲…的身份；站在…的地位；…的本身）

The position, *as such*, does not appeal to him, but the salary is a lure.

（他對那個職位本身並不感興趣，但是它的薪水卻很吸引他。）

⑲ **as well**（= also; too）（也）

Please take this **as well**.（這個也請拿去。）

⑳ **as well as**（= in addition to）（以及）

She wants a pen **as well as** a pencil.（她要一枝鋼筆和一枝鉛筆。）

㉑ **as yet**（= until now）（至今；尚）

I have received no answer from him **as yet**, but the answer will certainly come.
（我尚未收到他的回信，但回信一定會來。）

㉒ **in so far as**（視…而定）

You will learn your lessons only **in so far as** you are willing to study them.
（你的功課能學多少，完全視你肯用功的情形而定。）

㉓ **(just) as…, so…**（像…那樣；猶如）（詳見 p.502）

As the lion is king of beasts, **so** is the eagle king of birds.
（鷹為鳥中之王，猶如獅為萬獸之王一樣。）

㉔ **(just) as soon**（= rather）（寧願）

I would **just as soon** stay home.（我寧願留在家裡。）

㉕ **not** (*or* **never**) **so much as**（= not even）（連…都不）

I have **not so much as** heard his name.（我連他的名字都沒有聽說過。）

He **never so much as** enters a church.（他連教堂都沒進去過。）

【註】**without so much as** 後須接動名詞（片語）。

He left **without so much as** *saying "Thank you"*.
（他連「謝謝」都沒說就走掉了。）

㉖ **not such as to**（不致於）

His illness was **not such as to** cause any anxiety.（他的病尚不致於令人憂慮。）

㉗ **such as**（= for example）（像；如）（參照 p.478）

Languages, **such as** English and French, are not difficult to learn.
（語言，如英文、法文等，並不難學。）

2. **that** 的用法

(1) 做從屬連接詞，引導名詞子句。（詳見 p.479）

That *he should be ungrateful* cuts me to the heart.【that 子句做主詞】
（他竟忘恩負義，令我很傷心。）

O *that I knew the truth*!（我若知道這事實該多好啊！）【that 子句做受詞，詳見 p.370】
= I wish I knew the truth.

⑵ **做從屬連接詞，引導副詞子句。**

　　① 引導表「原因」的副詞子句。(詳見 p.511)

　　　If I find fault with your work, it is *that I want you to do better in the future.*
　　　(如果我挑剔你的工作，那是因為我要你將來做得更好。)

　　② 引導表「目的」的副詞子句。(詳見 p.513)

　　　I will do my best *that no lives may be lost.* (我會盡力不讓任何人喪生。)

　　③ 引導表「結果」的副詞子句。(詳見 p.516)

　　　He worked so hard *that he broke down.* (他太努力工作，以致於累壞了身體。)

　　　The difference is such (= so great) *that all will perceive it.*
　　　(差異非常大，以致於所有的人都能看得出來。)

　　【註】 *so much…that* 的語氣比 *so…that* 強；而 *so much so that* 的語氣又比 *so much…*
　　　　　that 更強。

　　　　　I am *so (much)* fatigued *that* I cannot work. (我累得無法工作。)

　　　　　He is very ignorant *so much so that he cannot read his own name.*
　　　　　　　　　　　　　　　　　　ignorant

　　　　　(他非常無知，無知到甚至連自己的名字都看不懂。)
　　　　　【句中第二個 so 是代替前面的敘述形容詞，再加 much 以避免兩個 so 在一起。本句因重複
　　　　　　說明兩次 very ignorant 所以是 He is so ignorant that…的加強語氣】

　　　　　Sometimes the cold was intense, *so much so that* raw eggs were frozen as hard
　　　　　　as if boiled.
　　　　　(天氣有時非常嚴寒，以致生蛋凍得好像煮過似地堅硬。)

　　　　　He is poor — *so much so that* he can hardly get enough to live.
　　　　　(他很窮，窮得幾乎無以維生。)

　　　　　The invalid was very tired when he returned from the ride; *so much so that* he
　　　　　　could not sit up.
　　　　　(病人坐車回到家的時候非常疲倦；疲倦得甚至無法坐起來。)

⑶ **做關係代名詞，引導形容詞子句。**(詳見 p.25, 152)

　　He is the greatest inventor *that ever lived.* (他是有史以來最偉大的發明家。)
　　　　　　　　　　　　　　　關代做主詞
　　We heard every word *that he said.* (我們聽到他說的每一個字。)

⑷ **代替關係副詞 when, where, why, how 引導形容詞子句。**(詳見 p.244)

　　I met him the year *that* (= *when*) *my uncle died.* (我遇見他是在我叔叔去世的那一年。)

⑸ **作副詞用相當於** *so*, *thus* 作「那麼；如此」解。

I will not go *that* far.（我不願走那麼遠。）
The baby cannot stay up *that* late.（這嬰兒不能那麼晚不睡。）

⑹ **做指示代名詞**，當主詞或當受詞。（詳見 p.122）

That is a red apple.（那是一個紅蘋果。）
I don't like *that*.（我不喜歡那個。）

⑺ **做指示形容詞**，用在名詞的前面。（參照 p.166）

That river runs rapidly.（那條河流得很急。）

⑻ **用在加強語氣的句型中**。（詳見 p.115）

It's Jean *that* makes the decision here.（這裡的事由琴做決定。）

⑼ **含有 that 的片語連接詞**。that 常和一些介詞或副詞而結合成片語連接詞，引導副詞子句。
（有關 that 的慣用語，參閱 p.123）

① *but that*

⒈ 作「而不」解，引導表「結果」的副詞子句。（詳見 p.519）

I am not so old *but that I may learn*.（我還沒老到不能學習的程度。）
= I am not so old *that I may not* learn.

⒉ 作「若非；如果不是因為」解，引導表「條件」的副詞子句。（詳見 p.522）

She would have fallen *but that I caught her*.（若非我拉住她，她早就掉下去了。）
= She would have fallen *if I had not* caught her.

② *except that*（除了…之外；只是）（參照 p.480）

It is a very satisfactory hat, *except that it doesn't fit me*.
（那是一頂令人滿意的帽子，只是不適合我。）

③ *for that*（因為；由於）（參照 p.510）

For that he is honest, we all like him.（由於他很誠實，我們大家都喜歡他。）

④ *in that*（= because）（因為）（詳見 p.510）

In that he killed a man, he was a murderer.（因為他殺死了一個人，所以他是個兇手。）

⑤ $\left\{ \begin{array}{l} not\ but \\ not\ but\ that \\ not\ but\ what \end{array} \right\}$（雖然）（參照 p.532）

I can't help her, *not but that I pity her*.（我雖然可憐她，但我不能幫助她。）
= I can't help her, though I do pity her.

⑥ ***now that*** (= since)（因為；既然）(詳見 p.510)

Now that *you mention it*, I do remember.

（因為你這樣一提，我就想起來了。）

⑦ ***only that*** (= were it not that)（如果不是…）(詳見 p.524)

I would go with you, ***only that*** *it is raining.*

（如果不是正下著雨，我一定跟你去。）

⑧ { ***save that*** / ***saving that*** }（除…之外）(參照 p.480)

He did well ***save that*** *he failed in Latin.*

（他除了拉丁文不及格之外，其他都考得很好。）

Saving that *he failed in Latin*, he did well.

（他除了拉丁文不及格之外，其他都考得很好。）

⑨ ***seeing*** (***that***)（因為；既然）(參照 p.510)

Seeing (***that***) *he refused to help us*, there is no reason why we should now help him.

（他既然曾經拒絕幫助我們，我們現在沒有理由要來幫助他。）

⑩ ***so that***

1. 引導表「目的」的副詞子句，作「為了；以便」(= in order that) 解。(詳見 p.513)

Speak clearly, ***so that*** *they* may *understand you.*

（說話清楚些，以便他們能聽懂你的話。）

2. 引導表「結果」的副詞子句，作「所以」(= so) 解。(詳見 p.518)

He spoke clearly, ***so that*** *everyone could hear.*

（他說得很清楚，所以每個人都聽到了。）

3. 引導表「條件」的副詞子句，作「只要」(= so long as) 解。(詳見 p.523)

So that *it is true*, what does it matter who said it?

（只要確實，是誰說的又有什麼關係？）

3. **but** 的用法

(1) **做連接詞**

① **做對等連接詞** (參閱 p.467, 470, 471, 474)

He is not *a writer*, ***but*** *a critic*.（他不是作家，而是批評家。）

He is old, ***but*** he is healthy.（他的確年老，但很健康。）

② 做從屬連接詞

　　/. **引導名詞子句**。(參照 p.24, 486)

　　　　　　　　　　名詞子句做受詞
　　　　Who knows *but he may go*? (誰知道他會不會去？)

　　&. **引導副詞子句表結果**。(詳見 p.519)

　　　　Never does a month pass *but she writes to her old parents.*
　　　　(她從來沒有超過一個月不給她年邁的雙親寫信的。)

(2) **做準關係代名詞** —— 即引導形容詞子句。(詳見 p.25, 160)

　　There is no one *but knows that.* (沒有人不知道那件事。)

(3) **做副詞**：用在動詞之後，或形容詞、副詞之前，相當於 only。

　　He is *but* a child. (他只是個小孩。)
　　He comes *but* seldom. (他難得來。)

(4) **做介詞** (參照 p.564)

　　but 用在前面有 no one, none, nothing 等否定字、who 等疑問詞，或 all, everyone 等字的
　　句子中，意義等於 except。此種用法的 but 還保有著連接詞的性質，所以後面可以接主格
　　或受格代名詞。

　　No one *but he* (*him*) showed much interest in the proposal.
　　(除了他以外，沒有一個人對這項提議感興趣。)

　　Nothing *but disaster* could come from such a plan.
　　(這計劃只有招致災禍，別無益處。)

　　Who *but he* would do such a thing? (除了他以外，還有誰會做這種事？)

(5) **含有 but 的慣用語：**

　　① *but for* (若非；如果沒有)【是片語介詞引導副詞片語，主要子句用假設法】

　　　　But for your help we would not have finished in time.
　　　　(如果沒有你的幫忙，我們就無法及時完成。)

　　② *but that*

　　　　a. 當從屬連接詞，引導名詞子句。(詳見 p.486)
　　　　b. 當從屬連接詞，引導表「結果」的副詞子句。(詳見 p.519)
　　　　c. 當從屬連接詞，引導表「條件」的副詞子句。(詳見 p.522)
　　　　d. 當從屬連接詞，引導表「讓步」的副詞子句。(詳見 p.532)

③ ***but then***（不過；在另一方面）

London is a noisy place, ***but then*** it's also the place where you get the best entertainment.

（倫敦是一個嘈雜的地方，不過它也是能獲得最佳娛樂的地方。）

④ ***all but***（幾乎）

He ***all but*** died of his wounds.（他幾乎因受傷而死。）

⑤ ***anything but***（絕不）

He is ***anything but*** a poet.（他絕不是個詩人。）

⑥ ***nothing but***（只是）

We could see ***nothing but*** fog.

（我們除了霧以外，看不見任何東西。）

⑦ ***indeed…but***（固然…但）（參照 p.471）

Indeed he is young, ***but*** he is careful.

（他固然年輕，但很仔細。）

⑧ ***it is true…but***（的確…但是）（參照 p.471）

It is true I went there, ***but*** I saw no one.

（我的確去過那裡，但我沒有見到任何人。）

⑨ ***may…, but…***（也許…但是…）

He ***may*** be a scholar, ***but*** he doesn't know everything.

（他也許是個學者，但並非什麼事都知道。）

⑩
first but one (***two, three***…)	〔第二（三，四…）〕
next but one (***two, three***…)	〔下面第二（三，四…）〕
last but one (***two, three***…)	〔倒數第二（三，四…）〕

He is the ***first but one*** to arrive.（他是第二個到達的。）

Take the ***next*** turn ***but one*** on your left.

= Take the second turn on your left.

（在你左方第二個轉彎處轉彎。）

I live in the ***last*** house ***but two*** on this street.

= I live in the third house from the end on this street.

（我住在這條街上倒數第三家。）

⑪ ***not that…but that…***（= not because…but because…）（不是因為…而是因為）（詳見 p.512）

I don't want any more, ***not that I don't like it***, ***but that I am just full and cannot eat anything more***.

（我不要再吃了，並不是因為我不喜歡吃，而是因為我吃得太飽了，再也吃不下了。）

4. *than* 的用法

(1) **做從屬連接詞** —— 引導表比較的副詞子句。(詳見 p.200, 201, 202)

John is taller *than his brother* (*is*). (約翰比他弟弟高。)

(2) **做準關係代名詞** —— 引導形容詞子句。(詳見 p.159)

He spends more money *than I earn*. (他花的錢比我賺的多。)

(3) **做介詞** —— 常與 whom 連用。

He is a person *than whom I can imagine no one more courteous*.
(我想不出一個比他更有禮貌的人。)

Here is my son, *than whom a better does not exist*.
(這就是我的兒子，世上再沒有比他更好的兒子了。)

(4) **含有 *than* 的慣用語**：(其他有關 than 的慣用語在 p.203)

① *more than* 可放在動詞之前，表示強調，作「非常…；多過…；不只…」解，等於 very,
not just。

This *more than* satisfied me. (這使我非常滿意。)

He has *more than* repaid my kindness. (他的回報多過我給他的恩惠。)

② *more than enough* (很多；太多；較需要者為多)

enough 在此為名詞，more than = over

A: Have you had enough to eat? (你有足夠的東西可吃嗎？)

B: Thank you, I've had *more than enough*. (謝謝你，我有很多。)

③ ⎧ *other* ⎫
　 ⎨ *otherwise* ⎬ *than* (= except; but) (除了)，但 ⎧ *otherwise* ⎫ *than* 較少用
　 ⎩ *else* ⎭ 　　　　　　　　　　　　　　　　　 ⎨ *else* ⎬
　　　　　　　　　　　　　　　　　　　　　　　　　 ⎩　　　 ⎭

⎧ I can think of no example *other than* this one.
⎪ = I can think of no *other* example *than* this one.
⎨ = I can think of no example *but* this one.
⎩ (除了這個例子之外，我想不出別的例子來。)

⎧ You can't get there *other*(*wise*) *than* by swimming.
⎨ = You can't get there *except* by swimming.
⎩ (除了游泳外，你沒有其他辦法到達那裡。)

⎧ He did *nothing else than* laugh.
⎨ = He did *nothing but* laugh.
⎩ = He *only* laughed. (他只是笑。)

【註】 *other than* 還可作「**與…不同的**」解，等於 different from。

I do not wish him *other than* he is. 【than 和 as 後 what 常省略】
= I do not wish him *different from* what he is.
(我不希望改變他的現狀 —— 他的現狀很好。)

請立刻做　練習九～十四

練 習 一 【第八篇動狀詞 p.409～463】

請改正下列各題句子中的錯誤。（用最少的字數）

1. I was used to go to the cinema once a week.

2. He has never been heard speak ill of others.

3. We hear it say frequently that what present-day men most desire is security.

4. He always enjoys to read a detective story.

5. His father would not let him to go.

6. It is difficult to make yourself understand in English.

7. You should avoid to keep company with such people.

8. Smiling graciously, my offer was accepted by him.

9. You had better not to go there.

10. The doctor advised me giving up to smoke.

11. I am going to have my watch mend.

12. I must remember seeing him tomorrow.

13. Comparing with his brother, he is not so intelligent.

14. A drowned man will catch at a straw.

15. His house, situating on a hill, commands a fine view.

16. Would you mind close the window?

17. I don't feel like to study tonight.

【解答】

1. was used → **used**，「used to + 原形動詞」作「從前」解；「be used to + （動）名詞」作「習慣於」解。

2. speak → **to speak**，感官動詞及使役動詞改為被動時，要用 to 形成不定詞片語，做主詞補語。

3. say → **said**，*We hear it said…that…*.   4. to read → **reading**，enjoy + ～ing。   5. to go → **go**，使役動詞後用原形動詞做受詞補語。   6. understand → **understood**，*make oneself understood*「使人了解某人自己的意思」，*understood* 前面省略了 *be*。（詳見 p.421）   7. to keep → **keeping**，*avoid* + ～*ing*「避免…」。   8. my offer was accepted by him → **he accepted my offer**，分詞構句 *Smiling graciously* 的意義主詞是 *he*，不是 *my offer*。   9. to go → **go**，*had better (best)* + 原形動詞「最好…」。   10. giving up to smoke → **to give up smoking**，*advise* + 受詞 + *to* + 原形，*give up* + ～*ing*。

11. mend → **mended**，*have* + 受詞 + *p.p.*。（詳見 p.454）   12. seeing → **to see**，*remember* + ～*ing* 表動作已發生；接不定詞表動作尚未發生。   13. Comparing → **Compared**（= When he is compared）

14. drowned → **drowning**，*a drowning man*「快淹死的人」，*a drowned man*「已經淹死的人」。（詳見 p.449）   15. situating → **situated**，situated on a hill（= which is situated on a hill）。

16. close → **closing**，*mind* + ～*ing*。   17. to study → **studying**，*feel like* + ～*ing*。

練 習 二 【第八篇動狀詞 p.409～463】

請改正下列各題句子中的錯誤。（用最少的字數）

1. We heard those Americans to speak in good Japanese.

2. He was heard say so.

3. My parents made me to go to school every day.

4. I advised him to not go there.

5. Here you are allowed talking in a loud voice.

6. He did nothing but to smile.

7. This poem is too difficult for me to understand it.

8. Will you help me moving the table?

9. I am not rich to keep a car.

10. It is very nice with you to think of me.

11. This is the classroom for us to study.

12. We had not better to say so.

13. He was seen enter the room.

14. This book is too hard to me to read.

15. They gradually became to enjoy their English lessons.

16. This book is cheap enough for him to buy it.

【解答】

1. to speak → *speak* (or *speaking*)，*heard* 是感官動詞，後面要用原形不定詞做受詞補語。（詳見 p.420）
2. say → *to say*，被動語態中，感官動詞後面的不定詞不可省略 *to*。（詳見 p.420）　　3. to go → *go*，使役動詞之後接原形不定詞做受詞補語。　　4. to not → *not to*，否定副詞該放在不定詞之前。
5. talking → *to talk*，*allow sb. to* + 原形動詞，改為被動語態為 *sb. be allowed to* + 原形動詞。（詳見 p.437）
6. to smile → *smile*，*do nothing but* + 原形動詞。　　7. to understand it → *to understand*，*This poem* 已是 *to understand* 的意義上受詞，後面不須再加 *it*。（詳見 p.411）　　8. moving → *(to) move*，*help* 接有 *to* 或沒 *to* 的不定詞皆可。（詳見 p.421）　　9. rich to → *rich enough to*（詳見 p.417）　　10. with → *of*（詳見 p.410）　　11. to study → *to study in* = *in which to study*（詳見 p.418）　　12. had not better to say → *had better not say*，*had better* + 原形動詞，*had better* 的否定詞 *had better not*。（參照 p.305）
13. enter → *to enter* (or *entering*)（理由同第 2. 題）　　14. to me → *for me*，不定詞 *to read* 意義上的主詞要用受格形。（詳見 p.410）　　15. became → *came*，*become* 後不可接不定詞，*come to* + 原形動詞或 *become* + p.p. 表示「轉變」。（詳見 p.387）　　16. buy it → *buy*（理由參照第 7. 題）

練 習 三 【第八篇動狀詞 p.409～463】

請改正下列各題句子中的錯誤。（用最少的字數）

1. I could not help laugh at it.

2. I am looking forward to see you soon.

3. Remember mailing the letter on your way to school.

4. I was not used to do such a thing.

5. He was prevented to take the entrance examination because of illness.

6. He always avoids to make any mistake.

7. I object to be treated like this.

8. I finished to read the book last night.

9. He insisted to go himself.

10. Unless you two stop to fight, I'll call in the police.

11. The law prohibits minors to smoke.

12. No one has ever succeeded to explain this phenomenon.

13. This book is worth to read.

14. Tell me the best way which to express my thanks.

15. I will have him taken my photograph.

【解答】

1. laugh → *laughing*，*cannot help* + ～*ing*「不得不…；忍不住…」。(詳見 p.441)　　2. see → *seeing*，*look forward to* + ～*ing*「盼望；期待」。　　3. mailing → *to mail*，「*remember* + ～*ing*」表示動作已經發生，「*remember* + *to* + 原形」表示動作尚未發生。(詳見 p.435)　　4. do → *doing*，*be used to* + ～*ing*「習慣於…」。　　5. to take → *from taking*，*prevent sb. from* ～*ing*「阻止某人…」，改成被動語態為 *sb. be prevented from* ～*ing*。　　6. to make → *making*，*avoid* + ～*ing*「避免」。　　7. be → *being*，*object to* + ～*ing*「反對」。　　8. to read → *reading*，*finish* + ～*ing*。　　9. to go → *on going*，*insist on* + ～*ing*。10. to fight → *fighting*，「*stop* + ～*ing*」表示「停止做某事」；「*stop to* + 原形」表示「停下來，去做某事」；*call in*「請來」。　　11. to smoke → *from smoking*，*prohibit sb. from* ～*ing*「禁止某人（做某事）」，*minor*「未成年者」。　　12. to explain → *in explaining*，*succeed in* + ～*ing*「（做某事）成功」。13. to read → *reading*，*be worth* + ～*ing*。(詳見 p.443)　　14. which to express → *to express*，the best way (*in which*) to express my thanks，*in which* 習慣上都省略。　　15. taken → *take*，「*have* + 人 + 原形」表主動。本句可改成 *I will have my photograph taken by him.* (詳見 p.454)

練 習 四 【第八篇動狀詞 p.409～463】

請改正下列各題句子中的錯誤。（用最少的字數）

1. Some chickens are chasing each other near the new mowing hay.

2. One of his articles described his travel in Europe is lost.

3. It's only a joke — nothing to be angry.

4. Spoken properly, the subject doesn't belong to grammar.

5. There is no deny the fact.

6. I got my car to be shined in the garage.

7. Newspaper accounts of international affairs are sometimes distorting.

8. He has lost so much time to consult his first cousins that he has no more time left to follow their advice.

9. Modern inventions, mass media and improving means of communication have helped to make the world smaller.

10. It struck her that she couldn't risk to lose the opportunity.

11. He stared a moment at his watch, his spirit was complaining at the job ahead of him.

12. They were prepared of leave when you telephoned.

13. Della had no choice but crying.

14. Look at the old sailor's frost-biting hands.

15. Schubert's friends had "The Erl-King" publish by subscription.

【解答】

1. new mowing → **new-mown** (or **newly mown**)「新割的」，「形容詞＋過去分詞」形成複合形容詞。（參照 p.450） 2. described → **describing** (= which describes)（詳見 p.457） 3. to be angry → **to be angry about**，nothing 是 to be angry about 意義上的受詞。（詳見 p.412） 4. Spoken properly → **Properly speaking**「正確地說」。（詳見 p.463） 5. no deny → **no denying**，There is no + ～ing = It is impossible to + 原形動詞。（詳見 p.439） 6. to be shined → **shined**，get + 物 + p.p.。（詳見 p.454） 7. distorting → **distorted**「被曲解」，依句意該用被動。 8. to consult → **(in) consulting**，lose time (hours,…) + (in) ～ing「浪費時間（做）…」。（參照 p.547） 9. improving → **improved**，表被動該用過去分詞。 10. to lose → **losing**，risk + ～ing。（詳見 p.436） 11. was complaining → **complaining**，兩個子句無連接詞是不對的，須改成「分詞構句」。（詳見 p.459） 12. prepared of leave → **prepared to leave**，of 不能接原形動詞，prepared to leave，不定詞（片語）可修飾動詞表目的。（詳見 p.413） 13. crying → **to cry**，have no choice (alternative) but + to + 原形。 14. frost-biting → **frost-bitten**「凍傷的」；frost-biting「駕滑冰船」。（詳見 p.450） 15. publish → **published**，have + 物 + p.p.。

練 習 五 【第八篇動狀詞 p.409～463】

請改正下列各題句子中的錯誤。（用最少的字數）

1. Wearing nothing but a light sweater, the cold wind drove me indoors.

2. He repents of being idle in his youth.

3. Your postcard, having addressed to the wrong house, never reached me.

4. Seeing from a distance, it looked like a human face.

5. Having read the book, it was thrown away by her.

6. I am sorry to have kept you waited so long.

7. However loud I spoke, I could not make myself hear.

8. I must have my room sweep.

9. I had my house break into.

10. The poison, using in a small quantity, will prove to be a medicine.

11. I had cut my hair at the barber's.

12. It was so still that you could have heard a pin to drop.

13. He is made study English by his father.

14. He insisted on I paying for it.

15. She is busy to cook the dinner.

16. His story was so disappointed that I went out of the room unobserved.

【解答】

1. the cold wind drove me indoors → ***I was driven indoors by the cold wind***，分詞構句前後主詞須一致。(詳見 p.458)　　2. being idle → ***having been idle***，*repent of* + (動)名詞「後悔」，用完成式動名詞表示比主要動詞早的狀態。　　3. having addressed → ***having been addressed*** (= *which had been addressed*)，須用被動語態。(詳見 p.462)　　4. Seeing → ***Seen*** (= *If it was seen*)(詳見 p.458)

5. it was thrown away by her → ***she threw it away***，分詞構句前後主詞須一致。(詳見 p.458)

6. waited → ***waiting***，*keep* + 受詞 + ~*ing*「使…繼續…」，用現在分詞表主動。(詳見 p.453)

7. make myself hear → ***make myself heard***「使自己被聽到」，*make* + 受詞 + *p.p.* 表被動。(詳見 p.453)

8. sweep → ***swept*** (理由同第 7. 題)　　9. break → ***broken*** (理由同第 7. 題)　　10. using → ***used*** (= *which is used*)(理由同第 3. 題)　　11. had cut my hair → ***had my hair cut***，*have* + 物 + *p.p.* 表示自己不做，而讓他人做。　　12. to drop → ***drop***，感官動詞之後用原形不定詞。(詳見 p.420)

13. study → ***to study***，使役動詞 *make* 為被動式時，其後不定詞的 *to* 不可省。(參照 p.420)

14. I paying → ***my paying***，人稱代名詞做動名詞的意義主詞，用所有格的形式。(詳見 p.427)

15. busy to cook → ***busy (in) cooking***，*be busy (in)* ~*ing*「忙於…」。(參照 p.547)

16. disappointed → ***disappointing***「令人失望的」。(詳見 p.194)

練 習 六 【第八篇動狀詞 p.409～463】

請改正下列各題句子中的錯誤。（用最少的字數）

1. I found impossible to go any farther.

2. He has more money than he knows to spend.

3. I saw a motorcar passes at full speed.

4. I hear a bird sings in the garden.

5. Father told me don't trouble him any more.

6. Would you kindly let me to know as soon as possible?

7. His father would have him to go to sea.

8. To be surely, he is a man of ability.

9. I never heard French speaking.

10. Written my composition, I have nothing else to do.

11. Being rainy, he did not start.

12. This did, he appeared to be satisfied.

13. Judging from he has not come, he may be on a trip.

14. It stopped to rain.

【解答】

1. → I found **it** impossible *to go any farther.*（詳見 p.114）　2. knows to → **knows how to**，how to spend 做 knows 的受詞；準關代 than 以 money 為先行詞，且為 spend 的受詞。（詳見 p.241, 161）
3. passes → **pass**，saw 是感官動詞，接原形不定詞做受詞補語。（詳見 p.420）　4. sings → **sing**，hear 是感官動詞。（理由同上題）　5. don't trouble → **not to trouble**，tell sb. (not) to do「告訴某人（不要）做…」，否定副詞該放在不定詞之前。（詳見 p.422）　6. to know → **know**，使役動詞 let 後接原形不定詞。（詳見 p.420）　7. to go → **go**，使役動詞 have 之後，接原形不定詞。（詳見 p.421）
8. To be surely → **To be sure**（= Surely; Certainly），sure 是 to be 的補語，構成不定詞片語，當獨立不定詞用。（詳見 p.15, 409, 417）　9. speaking → **spoken**（詳見 p.454）　10. Written → **Having written**，完成式分詞表分詞動作發生在主要子句動詞之前。（詳見 p.458, 461）　11. Being rainy → **It being rainy** (or **As it was rainy**)（詳見 p.462）　12. This did → **Having done this**（= As he had done this），或改為 **This having been done**（= As this had been done）。　13. Judging from → **Considering** (that) 或 **Seeing** (that)「因為；鑒於」，有幾個分詞可當連接詞用（詳見 p.510），Judging from「由…看來」，是非人稱獨立分詞片語。（參照 p.463）　14. stopped to rain → **stopped raining**（詳見 p.436）

練 習 七 【第八篇動狀詞 p.409～463】

請根據句意及文法選出一個最正確的答案。

1. The ceiling was arched, and _____ the frescoes the artist had to lie on his back on a high scaffolding.
   (A) painted　　　(B) painting　　　(C) to paint　　　(D) ×

2. A friend is someone whose loyalty you can _____.
   (A) take it for granted
   (B) take that for granting
   (C) take for granted
   (D) take for granting

3. I thought I had done the best thing I could _____.
   (A) to help her　　(B) help her　　(C) of helping her　　(D) not but help her

4. There is no _____ children.
   (A) humoring spoiled　(B) humoring with　(C) spoiling in　　(D) humor on the

5. _____ before the King and Queen, he told the story of his voyage.
   (A) To seat　　(B) Seating himself　(C) Seat　　　(D) Seating

6. The customs and laws _____ the aspects of the people's life must be understood.
   (A) relating to　　(B) relating　　(C) which relating with　(D) related with

7. A button has come off my shirt; I had better have it _____.
   (A) sewed on　　(B) sew in　　(C) sewing on　　(D) sewing

8. The policeman was killed _____ the gang.
   (A) while resisted
   (B) while he resisting
   (C) while resisting
   (D) while resistance to

9. Dr. Benson sat up on his bed, _____ the cold floor for his house slippers.
   (A) his feet feeling along
   (B) and his feet feeling along
   (C) with his feet felt along
   (D) but his feet felt with

【解答】

1. (C)，to paint the frescoes 當副詞用，修飾主要動詞 lie 表目的。(B) 改成 when painting 句意才明確。

2. (C)，take sth. for granted「視…為理所當然」，本句中 take 的受詞為 whose loyalty，如要用 it，須寫成 You can take *it* for (= *to be*) granted *that a friend is loyal.*　3. (A)，to help her 當副詞用，修飾動詞 done 表目的。　4. (A)，There is no + ～ing = We cannot + 原形「不能…；…是不可能的」(詳見 p.439)，本句直譯「不能縱容寵壞小孩」，humor (v.t.) 在此作「縱容；討好」解，spoiled children「被寵壞的小孩」。

5. (B)，seating himself = sitting，分詞構句代替第一個對等子句。(詳見 p.459)　　6. (A)，*relating to* 已轉化成片語介系詞「關於；有關」= *about*。　　7. (A)，have it sewed on (*my shirt*) (詳見 p.454)，sew a button on「把扣子縫到…上」。　8. (C)，while (*he was*) resisting，resist (v.t.)「抵抗」(詳見 p.462)，(A) → while he resisted，(D) → while offering resistance to。　9. (A)，and his feet felt along… = *his feet feeling along*…，對等子句改成分詞構句的方法在 p.459，(C) → with his feet feeling along。

練 習 八 【第八篇動狀詞 p.409～463】

請於空格部分填入一個適當的字。

1. What a fool you are _____ do such a thing!

2. I am sorry not to _____ answered your letter sooner.

3. He is too wise not _____ know it.

4. I awoke one morning _____ find the whole place covered with snow.

5. You had better _____ let him go when you were asked to.

6. You look tired. Don't you feel _____ having a short rest?

7. I could not _____ wondering at their vanity.

8. I cannot look at this photograph without _____ reminded of my dead brother.

9. The witness denied _____ seen the accused.

10. We speak of good people _____ to heaven, and wicked people to hell.

11. There _____ no bus service, we had to walk all the way to the inn.

12. _____ all things into consideration, he was a happy man.

13. The policeman came too late and found the thief _____ and the room in disorder.

14. Of my grandmother I knew only that she had never had her picture _____ in her lifetime.

【解答】

1. to，不定詞片語表示理由。(詳見 p.414)　　2. have，此句 = I am sorry *that I did not* answer your letter soon.　　3. to，*too…not to ～*「非常…不會不…」。(詳見 p.416)　　4. to，此處 *awoke* 後接表結果的不定詞片語。(詳見 p.414)　　5. have，*had better have* + 過去分詞「最好～了」，是對過去的事而言。　　6. like，*feel like* + ~*ing*「想要～」。(詳見 p.439)　　7. help，*cannot help* + ~*ing* = *cannot but* + 原形 V「不得不～；忍不住～」。(詳見 p.419, 441)　　8. being，*not…without* + ~*ing*「每…必定～」(詳見 p.440)；*be reminded of ～*「想起～」。　　9. having，*deny* 須以動名詞為受詞，又此句是指過去的事，故用「*deny having* + 過去分詞」。(參照 p.436)　　10. going，*go to heaven*「上天堂」接於 *of* 之後，故以動名詞表示。*good people* 為 *going* 的意義主詞。*wicked people* 後省略了 *going*。
11. being，是由 *As there was* no bus service 所改成的獨立分詞構句。(詳見 p.462)　　12. Taking，是由 *take…into consideration*「考慮」變成的獨立分詞片語，其主詞不是 *he*，而是「一般人」。(詳見 p.463)
13. gone，*found the thief gone* 是由 *found that the thief was gone* 變來的，*gone* 做 *the thief* 的補語。
14. taken，*take a picture*「照相」，have + 物 + p.p. 表示自己不做而讓別人做。

練 習 九 【第九篇連接詞 p.464～542】

請改正下列各題句子中的錯誤。（用最少的字數）

1. We become more and more impatient of interruptions when the years go on.

2. It was not until it began to rain when I noticed his umbrella left in my car.

3. At the age of six, my father took me to the circus for the first time.

4. You'll be permitted to bring a watch so that you may keep track of the time during you are taking the test.

5. It was not long since they made their appearance.

6. It was not so much the amount of the money but the money itself that surprised him.

7. There may not be much choice between this one or that.

8. We must eat for we may live.

9. Which do you like better, coffee and black tea?

10. Nothing is so hard that it becomes easy by practice.

11. The reason why he was absent is because he was ill.

12. No sooner had he left, it began to rain.

13. My father asked that what grade I had got for English.

14. I had reached the school till the bell rang.

15. He asked me there was any danger.

【解答】

1. when → **as**，依句意為「隨著…」，所以該用 as，不可用 when。（詳見 p.490） 2. when → **that**，It is (was) not until…that，是 not…until 的加強語氣形式。 3. At the age of six → **When I was six years old**，原句 At the age of six 是指 my father，句意不合。 4. during → **while**，during 是介系詞。 5. since → **before**（或 made → **had made**），not long before (or when)「…不久，就…」。（詳見 p.495） 6. but → **as**，not so much…as「與其說…不如說…」。 7. or → **and**，between…and…「在…和…之間」。 8. for → **that**，that (so that, in order that) + may (might)「為了…」是表目的的從屬連接詞；for 為表原因的對等連接詞。 9. and → **or** 是表選擇的連接詞。 10. that → **but**（= that…not）。（詳見 p.519） 11. because → **that**（或將 because 去掉）。（詳見 p.509） 12. left, it → **left than it**，no sooner…than「一…就…」。 13. that what → **what**，連接詞不可重複使用。 14. till → **before**「在…之前」，till「一直到…才」。（或 had → **had not**）（詳見 p.491） 15. me there → **me if there**（or **me whether there**），if 或 whether 引導名詞子句，做 asked 的直接受詞。（詳見 p.485）

練 習 十

練 習 十 【第九篇連接詞 p.464～542】

請改正下列各題句子中的錯誤。（用最少的字數）

1. No man is so old that he may learn.

2. The fact which he is connected with the crime is known to all.

3. The refugees neither had food nor shelter.

4. It had no other fault but that of being too short.

5. I shall go without I hear from you.

6. I cannot understand except you speak more slowly.

7. He studied English during he was there.

8. The general was not only kind to his men but also to his enemies.

9. Neither wealth nor power alone produce happiness.

10. She did not answer and put the book on the table and went away.

11. It will rain, because the barometer is falling.

12. It is now four or five years that I last came here.

13. Let us close the door before the bus does not start.

14. I hadn't hardly spoken to him when he was gone.

15. I went to see the zoo during I stayed in Taipei.

16. He worked hard in order to his family may live in comfort.

17. He worked hard lest he should not fail in the examination.

【解答】──────────────────────────────────────

1. that → ***but***（＝that…not）「沒有…不」。（詳見 p.519）　　2. which → ***that***，The fact that…「…的事實」，that 所引導的名詞子句是 The fact 的同位語。　　3. neither had food → ***had neither food***，neither…nor…是對等連接詞，必須連接文法作用相同的字詞。（詳見 p.468）　　4. but → ***than***（或 no other → ***no***），than 用在 other, else, otherwise, different 等之後作「除了…之外」解，no other…than「除了…之外沒有…」，可改為 no…but（＝except）。　　5. without → ***unless***，unless 是連接詞，without 是介系詞。　　6. except → ***unless***，except 是介系詞。　　7. during → ***while***（or ***when***），during 是介系詞，while 是連接詞。（詳見 p.490）　　8. was not only kind → ***was kind not only***，not only…but also 是對等連接詞。　　9. produce → ***produces***，neither…nor…連接兩個主詞時，動詞之數與後者一致。（詳見 p.468）　　10. and put → ***but put***，根據句意該用 but。　　11. because → ***for***，because 表示直接的原因，for 表示附加或推斷的理由。（詳見 p.477）　　12. that → ***since***，此處依句意該用 since「自從…」。　　13. does not start → ***starts***，依句意該用肯定的。　　14. hadn't → ***had***，hardly 已表否定意義，不可與否定字連用。　　15. during → ***while***（or ***when***），during 是介系詞。　　16. in order to → ***in order that***；may → ***might***，因主要子句動詞為過去式。　　17. should not → ***should***，lest…should 已表否定目的，不可再加否定字詞。

練 習 十一　【第九篇連接詞 p.464～542】

請改正下列各題句子中的錯誤。（用最少的字數）

1. You need not go with me unless you are not free now.

2. It did not take long before the boat sank.

3. We all felt if we were going to cry.

4. He spoke so rapidly as we could not clearly understand him.

5. She turned her head away lest he should not see her tears.

6. His only fault is what he has no fault.

7. He refused to go except I went with him.

8. As to whether Shakespeare wrote this poem is a matter of dispute.

9. It will not be long when you and I meet again.

10. Unless he does not work harder, he will certainly fail.

11. I asked him to tell me that how much he paid a month for his son's tuition.

12. I am sure it will be dark before he doesn't get there.

13. It was not so much the failure of the plan but the plan itself that vexed him.

14. He is convinced of that the boy is honest.

15. No sooner had the words been spoken when he realized that he should have remained silent.

【解答】

1. unless → *if*（或 are not → *are*）　　2. did not take → *was not*（或 before the boat sank → *for the boat to sink*），*It is not long before*…「…不久，就…」；後面是以不定詞做主詞時，動詞才可用 take「花費」，即 *It takes*…*for* + 受詞 + *to* + 原形。　　3. if → *as if*「宛如；好像」。（詳見 p.371）　　4. as → *that*，*so*…*that* 是表示結果的連接詞。（詳見 p.516）　　5. should not → *should*，*lest*…*should* 已表示否定的目的，不可再加 *not*。（詳見 p.514）　　6. what → *that*，*what* 引導名詞子句時必有代名作用，*that* 引導名詞子句時沒有代名作用。（詳見 p.156）　　7. except → *unless*，*except* 是介系詞。　　8. As to whether Shakespeare wrote this poem → *Whether Shakespeare wrote this poem* (*or not*)，*dispute*「爭論」。*whether* 引導名詞子句做主詞，不可再做介系詞的受詞。　　9. when → *before* (or *until*)（詳見 p.495）　　10. does not work → *works*，根據句意，不可再加 *not*。　　11. that how → *how*，連接詞不可重複使用。　　12. doesn't get → *gets*，根據句意要用肯定。　　13. but → *as*，*not so much*…*as*…「與其說是…不如說是…」，相當於 *not*…*but*…「不是…而是…」。　　14. of → 刪掉，*that* 子句不可當介詞 *of* 的受詞。（詳見 p.480）　　15. when → *than*，*No sooner*…*than*（= *as soon as*）。（詳見 p.496）

練 習 十二 【第九篇連接詞 p.464～542】

請改正下列各題句子中的錯誤。（用最少的字數）

1. He nodded his head in silence, and his eyes bright with tears.

2. I can assure you that a message is really important, it will reach you sooner or later.

3. I never buy anything unless is really needed.

4. I would rather go to a hairdresser than to try to save time by cutting my hair myself.

5. Her scheme completely failed, so she lacked insight and prudence.

6. Unless I don't see it with my own eyes, I won't believe it.

7. Icy as was the road, John drove very fast.

8. A failure as he was in school, he was a success in business later.

9. As many people as they came were caught.

10. It is neither hot or dry on the mountain.

11. Can you remember who was it you sold them to?

12. Turn to the right, you will find the post office.

13. We expected to arrive earlier and our train was late.

14. The mechanization of farming has become so familiar in recent years as we often forget the many changes it has brought about.

【解答】

1. and → 刪掉，(and) his eyes (were) bright with tears. = his eyes (being) bright with tears. (詳見 p.459)　　2. a message is → *if a message is*，that 引導的名詞子句中的兩個子句缺連接詞，依句意須加 *if*。　　3. unless is → *unless it is*　　4. than to try → *than try*，*would* (or *had*) *rather* + 原形 + *than* + 原形「寧願…而不願」。(參照 p.419)　　5. so → *for*，依句意 *she lacked insight*…是理由，故要用 *for*。(詳見 p.476)　　6. Unless I don't → *Unless I*，*unless* 是 *if*…*not* 的加強語氣，不可再用否定。(詳見 p.520)

7. was the road → *the road was*，*Icy as the road was* = *Although the road was icy*。(詳見 p.529)

8. A failure → *Failure*，*Although he was a failure* = *Failure as he was*。(詳見 p.529)　　9. they → 刪掉，*As many people as came were caught.* 第二個 as 是準關代。(詳見 p.159)　　10. or → *nor*，*neither*…*nor*「既不…也不…」。　　11. who was it → *who it was*，名詞子句該用敘述句的形式（主詞 + 動詞）。…*who it was you sold them to*。　　12. you will → *and you will* (詳見 p.360, 466)

13. and → *but*，前後句意相反要用 *but*。(詳見 p.470)　　14. as → *that*，*so*…*that*「如此…以致於」。(詳見 p.516)

練 習 十三 【第九篇連接詞 p.464～542】

I. 請依照括弧內的提示，改寫下列句子。

1. Though he is rich, he works very hard. (Rich…)

2. He gave me not only clothes, but also food. (用 as well as 改寫)

3. As soon as he caught sight of me, he avoided me. (No sooner…than)

4. The moment he caught sight of me, he ran away. (用 Scarcely 改寫)

5. When thirty, for the first time he made up his mind to do his own work. (It was not…)

II. 請將下列各題中的兩個單句用連接詞改寫成一個句子。

6.
① Will he pay the money?
② I doubt it.

7.
① Make haste.
② You will be late.

8.
① It rained very hard.
② There was no going out.

9.
① He is a wise man.
② This is well known to all.

10.
① He was a very nice fellow.
② Everybody liked him.

【解答】

1. Rich *as* he is, he works very hard. (詳見 p.529)

2. He gave me food *as well as* clothes. *not only A but also B = B as well as A* (參照 p.467)

3. *No sooner* had he caught sight of me *than* he avoided me. (詳見 p.496)

4. *Scarcely* had he caught sight of me *when* he ran away. (詳見 p.496)

5. *It was not until* he was thirty *that* he made up his mind to do his own work.
   It was not until…that 「直到…才…」。(參照 p.492)

6. I doubt *if* he will pay the money. (詳見 p.481, 485)

7. Make haste, *or* you will be late. / *Unless* you make haste, you will be late. (詳見 p.473, 520)

8. *As* it rained very hard, there was no going out. / It rained very hard, *so* there was no going out. /
   There was no going out *because* it rained very hard. /
   It rained *so* hard *that* there was no going out. (參照 p.474, 507, 508, 516)

9. *That* he is a wise man is well known to all. / It is well known to all *that* he is a wise man. /
   He is a wise man, *as* is well known to all. (參照 p.160, 499, 479)

10. He was *such* a nice fellow *that* everybody liked him. /
    He was a very nice fellow, *so* everybody liked him. /
    Everybody liked him *because* he was a very nice fellow. (詳見 p.474, 508, 516)

練 習 十四 【第九篇連接詞 p.464～542】

請於下列空格填入一個適當的字。（有些空格已限定該字起首的字母）

1. It never rains _____ it pours.

2. _____ or not he is coming hasn't been decided yet.

3. I am not rich, _____ do I wish to be.

4. It was not long _____ he became aware of the danger.

5. Waking o_____ sleeping, this subject is always in my mind.

6. You must do it, _____ you like it _____ not.

7. It is ten years _____ I started learning English.

8. Poor a_____ he was, he was honest.

9. We must take into account the fact _____ he is unmarried.

10. She had not walked a mile _____ she got tired.

11. One step farther, _____ you will fall over the precipice.

12. I am an eager, _____ not a skillful, sportsman.

13. _____ that he is gone, we miss him very badly.

14. No sooner had I entered the room _____ he left it.

15. Take this medicine, _____ you will get over your cold.

16. I will take care of the child _____ long _____ I live.

17. Not only did I read the poem _____ I copied it.

18. I wonder i_____ it will be nice tomorrow.

19. Do tell me everything you know; o_____ I cannot help you.

【解答】

1. but，but 是具有否定意味的連接詞。**never…but**「沒有…不」。（詳見 p.470, 661）

2. Whether，引導名詞子句 "*Whether or not he is coming*" 做句子的主詞。（詳見 p.484）

3. nor。（詳見 p.468）　　4. before。（詳見 p.495）　　5. or。（參照 p.474）　　6. whether, or，*whether… or* 引導表示讓步的副詞子句時，意指「無論」。（詳見 p.524）　　7. since，「自從…以來」。（詳見 p.492）

8. as（= *though*），*Poor **as** he was* = ***Though** (**Although**) he was poor*。（詳見 p.529）

9. that，*that* 引導名詞子句做 *the fact* 的同位語。　　10. before（或 when）。（詳見 p.495）

11. and，此句意思為「再跨一步，你就會掉到懸崖下。」（詳見 p.466）　　12. if（或 though）「雖然」，if (though) not a skillful 是由 if (though) *I am* not a skillful 省略而來。　　13. Now，*now that*「既然」。（詳見 p.510）　　14. than，*no sooner…than*「一…就…」。（詳見 p.496）　　15. and。（詳見 p.466）

16. as, as，*as long as*「只要」。（詳見 p.520）　　17. but，*not only…but (also)* …「不但…而且…」。（詳見 p.467）　　18. if。（詳見 p.485）　　19. or（或 otherwise）。（詳見 p.474）

【附錄 —— 英文法盲點講座】

以下的句子，都是出自各校的月期考試題，老師有時因中外文化的差異，而造出錯誤的句子，這正是我們要注意的地方。

1. Cut the ham, and then put some salt.【木柵國中】

　　【解說】　① put → *add*

　　　　　　② put some salt → *put some salt on it*

　　　　　　本句重點在中外思想不同，中文較不精確，英文較直接。

　　　　　　中國人的思想：放點鹽（在上面）

　　　　　　美國人的思想：「加」點鹽（在上面）

2. I am hungry and I can eat a horse.【永平國中】

　　【解說】　and 不可表結果。（詳見 p.516）

　　　　　　→ I am hungry. I could eat a horse.

　　　　　　→ I am so hungry (that) I could eat a horse.

　　　　　　如果句子短，也可用逗點代替 that，寫成：

　　　　　　I am so hungry, I could eat a horse.

　　　　　　could eat a horse 吃很多【並非真的吃下一匹馬，所以用假設法助動詞 could】

3. Can the dog catch the dog?【石門國中】

　　【解說】　→ Can the dog catch *the other* dog?

　　　　　　本句錯在中外思想不同。

　　　　　　中國人的思想：狗抓狗

　　　　　　美國人的思想：狗抓「另一隻」狗

4. The weather for Friday will be cold.【北安國中】

　　【解說】　表星期幾、日期、特定的早、午、晚，用介詞 on。（詳見 p.591）

　　　　　　① → The weather *on* Friday will be cold.

　　　　　　② → The weather for *tomorrow* will be cold.

　　　　　　in the morning【一般，非特定】

　　　　　　on a fine morning【特定的早上】

　　　　　　on June 4th（在6月4日）【特定日期】

5. A: I'll go to the bookstore.

B: Oh, I like there, too. Can I join you?【延平國中】

【解說】 *I like there, too.* → *I like it there, too.*

中文： 你喜歡這裡嗎？

英文： *Do you like here?*【誤】

Do you like it here?【正】【it = life 或 being】
       vt.   *adv.*

Do you like this place?【正】

here, there 當名詞，是指一個點（**a point in space**），不是一個地方（像 **bookstore**）。

例如： Let's get out of **here**.（我們走吧。）
            n.

He lives near **here**.（他住在這附近。）
            n.

It's cold in **here**.（這裡很冷。）
           n.

How far is it from **here** to **there**?（從這裡到那裡有多遠？）
            n.   *n.*

I'll reach **there** tomorrow.（我明天將到達那裡。）
     vt.   *n.*

6. Always be a good student. Don't let your parents angry.【士林國中】

【解說】 ① → Don't let your parents **get** angry.（詳見 p.386, 421）

② → Don't **make** your parents angry.

let 和 **make** 的用法不同：

let + O + V 原【let 加受詞後，只能加原形動詞，除了 Don't let me down.（不要讓我失望。）例外】

$$make + O + \begin{cases} V \ 原 \\ adj. \\ N \end{cases}$$

Never make a pretty woman your wife.（絕對不要娶美女為妻。）

7. Joy's Kitchen opens every day.【頭前國中閱讀測驗】

【解說】 open *v.* 開門（動作）　*adj.* 營業的（狀態）

→ <u>Joy's Kitchen</u> opens *at 7:00 a.m.*
   ‖
   Joy's Restaurant

→ Joy's Kitchen *is open* every day.

8. The house is too expensive. We don't have so much money to buy it.

【解說】① → We don't have **enough** money to buy it. (詳見 p.170)

② → We **can't afford** to buy it.

中國人的思想：我們沒那麼多錢去買。

美國人的思想：我們沒有**足夠**的錢買。

我們**買不起**。

9. My brother always goes to school every morning. 【南門國中】

【解說】這句話是中式英文，必須去掉 always，或將 every morning 改成 **in the morning**，否則句意重覆，因為 every morning 已經表示「每天」了，不須再用 always。

10. She can see F4 face to face this Sunday. 【木柵國中閱讀測驗】

【解說】face to face → **in person** (面對面)

in person 有三個意思：①一對一面對 ②面對面 ③親自

face to face「一對一面對」，只有一個意思。

She met the members of F4 <u>face to face</u>.
　　　　　　　　　　　　　　║
　　　　　　　　　　　　in person

11. She eats some snacks and watch TV in the living room. 【北安國中】

【解說】① watch → **watches** (詳見 p.465)

② eat → **is eating**；watch → **watching**

and 是對等連接詞，在此應連接兩個文法地位相同的動詞。

12. Cats and dogs are all animals. 【西湖國中】

【解說】all → **both**【因為只有兩種動物，故須用 both】(詳見 p.133, 134)

Cats, dogs, and birds are all animals.【三種動物以上，才用 all】

中國人的思想：貓和狗都是動物。

美國人的思想：貓和狗**兩者**都是動物。

13. Jenny did her homework in time but her sister cannot. 【中正國中】

【解説】 cannot → **didn't** 或 **couldn't** (詳見 p.470)

but 是表反義的對等連接詞，前後動詞應一致。

14. You can shop in the department store. It's on sale today. 【大安國中】

【解説】 這句話句意不合理，應該是「百貨公司舉辦拍賣」，不是「百貨公司被拍賣」。

① It's on sale today. → **It's having a sale today**. 【It 指 The department store】

② It's on sale today. → **All clothing is on sale today**.

have a sale 舉辦特賣　　**on sale** 特價

中文的「大拍賣」，就是美國人的 on sale。

15. Be a good student, never go to school late. 【育林國中】

【解説】 ① → …, **and** never go late　to school. 【短副詞接近動詞】(詳見 p.269)
短　　　長

② → …, **and** never be late for school.

兩個動詞之間，需要連接詞。

16. Is there any restaurant in your school? 【景興國中】

【解説】 本句文法沒有錯誤，但句意不合理。any 可接單數或複數名詞，**any + 單數 N** 時，比 "**a**" 的語氣更強。

中文：你的學校有沒有餐廳？【正】

你的學校有沒有任何一家餐廳？【誤，一般人不會這麼說】

① → Is there a restaurant in your school?

② → Are there any restaurants in your school?

③ → Is there any restaurant in your school that sells hamburgers?

「any + 單數名詞」是指「任何一家」，這個句子的句意才合理。

17. I try some French food and enjoy it a lot. 【弘道國中】

【解説】 try → **tried**；enjoy → **enjoyed**

因為用現在式表示天天都吃，不合理。

18. May I have some drink?【南港國中】

【解說】 drink（酒；飲料）為可數名詞，water（水）為不可數名詞。（詳見 p.55）
① → May I have some **drinks**?（我可以喝一些飲料嗎？）
② → May I have **a drink**?（我可以喝杯酒嗎？）
③ → May I have some **water**?（我可以喝一些水嗎？）【some 可修飾單複數名詞】

19. The T-shirts are on sale. They are very cheap. And you buy one and get one free.【景興國中】

【解說】 And 去掉或改成 **In addition**,
You buy one and get one free.（買一送一。）
= Buy one, get one free.【慣用句】
= If you buy one, you get one free.

又如： Class dismissed.（下課。）【慣用句】
This class dismissed.【誤】
Class is dismissed.【誤】
This class is dismissed.【正】

20. There are many funny activities in the summer camp.【士林國中】

【解說】 ① funny → **fun**
funny *adj.* 可笑的
fun *adj.* 有趣的
② in the summer camp → **at summer camp**（在夏令營）【抽象名詞】
at 表「從事…活動」，如：at work（在工作），at school（在上學），at breakfast（在吃早餐）。（詳見 p.556）

21. Larry is a lazy student. He won't study until the night before the exams, so he seldom gets good grades. 老師問是否應將 won't study 改成 doesn't study 視為一種習慣？【金華國中】

【解說】 不需要改，因為 will 也可表「習性」。（詳見 p.308）
Boys will be boys.（男孩就是男孩。）
Accidents will happen.（天有不測風雲。）
the exams → **an exam**

22. Welcome to Taipei 101 and enjoy your shopping. 【中正國中】

【解說】 enjoy your shopping → **enjoy shopping**

動名詞已有意義上的主詞時,不須再有文法上的主詞。(詳見 p.426)

→ enjoy your visit 【正】

→ enjoy your shopping experience 【正】

23. Mark is watering. He is very hungry. 【石牌國中】

【解說】 → Mark**'s mouth** is watering.

中國人說「某人流口水」,美國人則說「某人的嘴巴流口水」。

water〔'wɔtə〕v. 流口水

24. I'm Tina in your class. 【和平國中】

【解說】 I'm Tina | in your class. | 這句話的意思是「在你的班上我是 Tina。

(在家也許我叫 Jennifer。)」,句意不合理。

① → I'm Tina **from** your class. (我是你們班的 Tina。)

又如:I'm a student from Taiwan. (我是台灣來的學生。)

② → I'm Tina and I'm in your class.

→ I'm Tina, in your class. 【沒有逗點是限定用法,有逗點是補述

用法,即對前面的話加以補充說明,參考 p.161, 162】

25. My teacher is from U.S.A. 【萬華國中】

【解說】 U.S.A. → **the U.S.A.**

專有名詞不加冠詞,但字尾有 s 的專有名詞要加 the。(詳見 p.63)

例如:the United Nations (聯合國),the Rockies (洛磯山脈)

the Alps (阿爾卑斯山脈),the Philippines (菲律賓;菲律

賓群島)。

26. Don't worry. I have a lot of money. I can pay the dinner tonight. 【和平國中】

【解說】 ① → I can pay **for dinner**. 【pay for 支付】

② → I can pay **the bill for** dinner. 【pay the bill 付帳】

普通 N 要加冠詞,但三餐名詞例外:breakfast, lunch, dinner,

supper。(詳見 p.222)